THE YOUNG MOZART

The Young Mozart

ALAN JENKINS

Illustrated by
Anne Linton

ROY PUBLISHERS · NEW YORK

Library of Congress Catalog Card Number: 61-11041

© 1961 ALAN JENKINS
MADE AND PRINTED IN GREAT BRITAIN BY
PURNELL AND SONS LTD PAULTON (SOMERSET) AND LONDON

For
ANNABEL
when she is a little older

Contents

I

The House of Music

The canary sang and sang. He always sang when someone was having a music lesson, which was nearly all day long, for Leopold Mozart taught both violin and clavier to the children of rich people in Salzburg.

This morning it was Marianne, his own daughter, who was sitting at the clavier. Nannerl, as the family called her, was nearly eight now, and had been learning for four years.

'One – two – *three* and *four* and one – two . . .' Papa Leopold counted aloud as he walked up and down the room. 'Don't rush it – carry the fourth finger over the thumb in that last triplet – look, I'll mark it with a cross so you won't forget it.'

Nannerl was always the calm one. She never got flustered – Papa was a kind teacher anyway – and she already had a firm, confident touch, and could tackle most of the pieces her father had copied out for her into a big, leather-bound manuscript book.

Papa was not so sure about little Wolfgang. He was only three, and perhaps in a year's time he too would be ready for music lessons. As long as someone was playing music, he would stay absolutely still, listening as if in a trance. But the moment the music stopped, he would be off again, tearing up and down the corridor, getting in his poor mother's way in the kitchen, leaning out of the window to see what was going on in the street – and nearly falling out too. It was as if he could never spend enough energy.

'Once more from the beginning, Nannerl, and I think that'll do for today,' Papa said. 'You needn't bother about the repeats. Now, one – two – *three* and *four* . . . not too fast, there's nobody chasing you.'

When the lesson was over, Nannerl went to the window and looked out. There was always somebody or something to watch in the Löchelplatz below. The Mozarts' flat was on the third floor, and if you had a good aim you could drop paper pellets on the heads of people beneath.

Nannerl listened to the plop-plop of the little fountain in the square, idly watching the women with their copper pails gossiping as they went to draw water. From the market square behind the house came the big bell of the church striking two o'clock. Sometimes it boomed so loudly that little Wolfgang stopped his ears and cried as if it hurt him.

But Wolfgang didn't seem to notice it today. He had scrambled on to Nannerl's stool at the clavier and was utterly absorbed in picking out phrases and tiny chords of his own invention.

'I can do it, I can do it!' he shouted triumphantly every time he struck a few notes that didn't sound too ugly.

'That's what *you* think, Wolfgang!' Nannerl turned from the window and smiled. 'You wait till you have to have lessons. You won't think it's much fun then.'

'I *can* do it!' Wolfgang's blue eyes were bright with sudden tears. He couldn't bear to be teased. 'Listen!'

He played G and E together, followed by E and C twice; then F and D together, followed by D and B twice. It was the first two bars of an old German nursery song called 'Little Hans'.

'Not bad, little brother,' Nannerl said soothingly. 'Not bad at all. Here, sit more comfortably.' She brought some books for him to sit on because the stool was too low. He looked so funny, perched on high, with his legs dangling so far above the pedals that he couldn't possibly have reached them. Nannerl wanted to laugh, but she controlled herself; little Wolfgang got furious if people laughed at his smallness.

'What was that piece you were playing, Nannerl?' he asked solemnly. 'The one that went like this?'

To Nannerl's amazement, he played the very phrase – the one with the difficult triplets – that Papa had made her repeat just before the end of her lesson.

'It's – it's a Passacaglia by Handel,' she gasped. 'But however did *you* learn it?'

'What's a Passacaglia?' he demanded.

'It's a sort of . . . But *you* were playing it, Wolferl!'

'I just watched how you did it and copied you,' Wolfgang said unconcernedly. 'Look, I can remember some
more of it!'

His tiny hands, too small to stretch more than five notes,
struggled over the keyboard. He even managed to fill in,
by ear, a few plonking notes in the bass.

'Nannerl!' Papa's voice came from the bedroom, where
he was washing his hands before dinner. 'That's enough
playing for today! You're getting worse and worse. Come
and wash your hands.'

'But, Papa!' Nannerl's voice squeaked with excitement.
'It isn't me playing! It's Wolfgang! He doesn't even
know his notes, but he's playing!'

Papa put his head round the door and stared.

'I *can* do it,' Wolfgang was saying crossly. 'I *told* you I
could, and you didn't believe me.' He rattled through the
whole tune again without stopping. 'There!'

Papa's head disappeared for a moment. They heard him
calling to Mamma in the kitchen. His voice shook with
delight. 'My dearest, come here quickly. Wolfgang has
something to show you!'

A nose-tickling smell of liver dumplings and sauerkraut,
the Mozarts' favourite dish, came wafting through the
apartment as the kitchen door was opened. Mamma
Mozart bustled in, wiping her hands on her apron. 'Dinner
will be ready in half a minute,' she began. 'Now, are you
all ready? I don't want it to get cold. Well, what's it all
about?'

Papa held up his finger for silence. With his tongue
stuck firmly out of the corner of his mouth, little Wolfgang played the difficult triplets again. Then he stood on
top of the books on the stool, shouting with laughter.
'Catch me, catch me, I'm going to jump!' and fell,
struggling and panting, into his mother's arms.

All Mamma said was, 'I expect you're hungry.'

'I'm so hungry I could eat an ox, and a whole house full of potatoes, and a mountain of cabbage, and –'

'Then come and eat, and don't waste so much time talking!' she laughed.

But during the meal Mamma and Papa Mozart looked thoughtful, and glanced from little Wolfgang to each other. And when the table was cleared and the dishes washed, and Wolfgang, suddenly tired, was having his afternoon rest, and Nannerl was doing her lessons, they sat down for a quiet talk before the next pupil arrived.

'What do you think?' Mamma whispered.

'I think that another Mozart will be able to earn his living by music.' Papa smiled in that cautious way of his.

'But at *three* years old!' she said. 'Do you remember how early he learned to walk and talk and count? Isn't this a wonder-child we have? Oh, God is good to us!' she sighed.

Papa nodded and rubbed his chin thoughtfully. He was remembering how little Wolfgang had struggled for life when he was a baby, and thinking how small he was for his age even now. They must take good care of him.

'You can't tell yet,' he said. 'Some children learn everything fast when they are very small, and when they grow up they're no different from others. And some children stay in the bottom class at school but somehow manage to become geniuses when they grow up.' Papa shrugged his shoulders and laughed. 'No one can tell!'

But Mamma could see that he was secretly delighted with his small son.

'One thing is certain,' he said. 'The boy must have music lessons. We'll start tomorrow.'

'Yes. Teach him *now*, while he is enthusiastic – while he really *wants* to learn!' she cried. 'So many children are

made to learn the clavier or the violin because it is supposed to be *good* for them, and they are forced to practise,
and so they come to hate music instead of loving it!'

'Like Miss Glasenbach, who will be coming for her
violin lesson in ten minutes' time,' said Leopold, looking
at the clock. 'The daughter of Alderman Glasenbach must
learn the violin because it is a suitable accomplishment for
an alderman's daughter. Four years I have been teaching
her, and she can't even play a scale without a mistake! At
least she comes to me, instead of my having to go to her
father's house.'

'If only you didn't have to give lessons!' his wife said
longingly. 'If only the Archbishop would make you
Director of Music instead of using you to teach the violin
to all those noisy choirboys of his! If only he would see
what a good composer you are –'

'If only, if only!' Leopold laughed. 'Well, he may do
that yet. But as long as I have pupils, we shan't starve. So
let's be thankful for them.'

There was a knock at the door. Leopold Mozart got up
to open it.

'Even for Miss Theresia Glasenbach,' he sighed.

*

A year went by, and another year. Leopold Mozart and
his wife could hardly believe their eyes and ears. People
stopped in the street outside to listen to Wolfgang's
playing.

'Herr Mozart must be a wonderful teacher,' they told
each other. 'He has a pupil who can play the clavier as
well as he does himself.' But they wouldn't believe it was
Wolfgang. How could a little boy of five play like that?
It was impossible. It was unheard of. No boy of five had
ever played like a professional musician before. Herr
Mozart must be pulling their legs.

'So you don't believe me?' Leopold Mozart used to shout out of the window. He got as angry as his small son when people didn't believe him. 'All right – come and hear for yourselves!'

And people came up to the third-floor flat, and took a glass of wine with the Mozarts, and shook their heads wonderingly. They saw a little boy, with a mop of fair hair falling around his cheeks, perched high on a special chair so that he could reach the keyboard. His tiny fingers flew up and down that keyboard as if they didn't belong to him at all, as if they were controlled by some kind of magic far away.

'I give you my word,' Leopold told his friends, 'I have already taught the boy nearly all I know about the clavier. But that isn't all. Do you know, I found him meddling with my violin the other day! I swear to you he played a few bars of a minuet on it without a mistake. He just picked up my fiddle, which he had never touched before, and played it!'

There was a roar of laughter. 'Oh, come, my good Leopold, this goes too far! You'll be telling us next that this lad wrote your book for you!'

Leopold's book on how to play the violin was well known all over Europe; it had been printed the year Wolfgang was born.

'Laugh if you will, my friends!' Leopold said. 'But it's true. I don't claim any credit for it. The boy has a gift – that is God's doing, not mine. He watches me playing the violin, sees how I place my fingers, and how I draw my bow across the strings, and he imitates me like a monkey. Is it so astonishing? After all, there are boys of his age who can beat a grown man at chess, or work out sums in their heads. It is a knack, you know, simply a knack.'

But, try as he would, Leopold Mozart could not hide his

pride and excitement at Wolfgang's skill. Next year, he would begin teaching the boy harmony, and how to compose tunes of his own; and after that, how to write music for three instruments, and four, and five; and after that, how to manage a whole orchestra . . .

'If he hasn't taught himself everything in the meantime!' Leopold smiled to himself.

To look at Wolfgang, you wouldn't think the boy was anything out of the ordinary. He shouted a lot, and clambered all over the furniture, and turned somersaults when he had nothing else to do; and if Papa or Mamma looked serious and thoughtful, he would do any crazy thing that came into his head, to make them burst out laughing.

Papa was often grave and thoughtful these days. Wolfgang climbed on his knee and pulled his nose and asked, 'Papa, why are grown-ups often so sad?'

'Because they have a lot of worries,' Leopold smiled.

'What sort of worries?' the boy asked.

'Well, they worry about – about what is to become of us all. They have to think of how to earn enough money to feed and clothe their children. They have to decide what is best to be done –'

The boy nodded solemnly. 'That must be very trying,' he said. '*I* shan't have worries when I grow up. I shall earn so much money that I shall be able to buy a castle for you and Mamma and Nannerl to live in when you are all very old, and when you die I shall have you stuffed and keep you in a glass case like the trout Herr Hagenauer caught, so that we shall always be together, and . . .'

Leopold shook with laughter. You couldn't be sad and serious for long with this funny little boy who said such extraordinary things.

'Papa, why don't we go fishing sometimes?' Wolfgang went on. 'The Salzach river must be full of fish.'

'Fishing, eh?' Leopold looked grave again. 'H'm. Well, we'll have to see.'

When Leopold said 'we'll have to see', you knew he either couldn't or wouldn't do anything about it. Now he was looking at his small son and thinking, 'Poor little chap, he doesn't get out into the fresh air enough. None of us does. Heigho! That's what it means to be a musician. You have to spend most of your life indoors, practising, practising, learning, teaching . . .'

Suddenly he said, 'Well, I don't think we can go fishing today. For one thing, we haven't any rods or bait. But look, the sun is shining! It's a beautiful afternoon. Let's have no lessons today, and go for a walk instead! What do you say?'

For answer, Wolfgang pulled Leopold to his feet and danced round and round him, shouting at the top of his voice. 'Can Nannerl come too, Papa? And Mamma as well?'

As if there wasn't enough noise already, someone began playing a trumpet in the flat above, and from a room at the back of the house came the sound of a 'cello playing the difficult bits of a quartet. For another trouble about being a musician is that you generally have to live in a house with other musicians because the neighbours, however much they like music, get pretty tired of hearing you practising.

Mamma Mozart came in to see what all the fuss was about. 'Oh, if only we could live in a house of our own!' she cried, holding her hands over her ears.

Her husband said, 'Wolferl is going to buy us a castle to live in when he grows up. That's thoughtful of him, isn't it?'

'Mamma, we are going for a walk in the country!' Wolfgang shouted. 'You'll come too, won't you?'

'Get along with you. I've far too much to do. But I'll be glad to have the place empty for an hour or two. Off you go!'

Going for a walk was much harder work than Wolfgang had imagined. When Papa said, 'Let's go for a walk in the hills,' Wolfgang at once imagined himself standing on top of a hill – say, the Kapuzinerberg on the north side of the river, or the Mönchsberg on the south – looking down on the little city and admiring the view. It never occurred to him that you had to climb the hill first, and that climbing was a slow business that took away your breath if you weren't used to it.

For the first half-hour he was so interested in everything he saw that he forgot to feel tired. First they crossed the Löchelplatz, with its funny old fountain where Mamma Mozart went to draw water for the kitchen. Here they met Herr Hagenauer, their landlord, who was astonished to see them. 'A *walk*?' he cried. 'Going for a *walk*? Why? Are you ill, and have to see a doctor? Or perhaps you need something from the market? Please let me send my servant instead.'

Nobody in Salzburg ever 'went for a walk' just for the sake of fresh air and exercise. If you were rich, and had a carriage with horses, you drove out into the country sometimes, taking a picnic with you. But walking when it wasn't necessary – no, the good people of Salzburg couldn't understand it. Why, you might do yourself harm, or get your clothes dirty! The way to keep fit was to take lots of medicines and pills, not go for walks. Anyway, Herr Hagenauer thought it was a great joke.

As the Mozarts came down the steps to the riverside, they heard a posthorn in the distance, and saw a cloud of dust on the bridge over the river.

'That's the Archbishop's carriage,' said Leopold. 'Drop

a curtsey as he comes by, Nannerl. And you, Wolfgang, don't forget to bow.'

The hoofbeats came nearer, and so did the cloud of dust. A moment later the carriage itself appeared out of the dust, and the children could see the black, red and gold colours of it, and the white periwigs of the footmen. Leopold swept off his hat and bowed deeply. So did little Wolfgang, and Nannerl curtsied gracefully. Whether the Archbishop saw them or not, they had no idea. Certainly they could not see the Archbishop. The carriage rattled on towards the Archbishop's Palace by the Cathedral, not far from where the Mozarts lived.

'Papa,' asked Wolfgang, as they continued their walk, 'why do we always have to bow and wave our hats whenever we meet the Archbishop? Anyone would think he was the Emperor.'

'We must show our respect to him because he is the Archbishop,' Leopold smiled. 'Besides, you don't want him to think that the Mozarts have no manners, do you? Also, we owe him a great deal. He pays me a few *gulden* a month to be one of his Court musicians, to write and arrange music for the Court Orchestra, to teach his choirboys to play the violin, and generally to make myself useful.'

'He doesn't pay you enough,' Wolfgang said. 'I've heard Mamma say so often.'

'He pays what he can, I suppose,' Leopold laughed. 'Well, perhaps he will give me a better position one of these days. Perhaps he will even make me his Director of Music – who knows? Then I could get rid of some of my pupils, and not have to work so hard.'

They had crossed the river now, and were beginning to climb the thickly-wooded slopes of the Capucine Hill. Wolfgang began to complain that his legs ached. Leopold offered to carry him, but the boy refused. 'I am too big to be carried,' he said with great dignity. 'Why, I am five years old!' Nannerl took his hand and pulled him up the hill, and this he did not seem to mind at all.

At last they got to the top, and sat on the grass, panting. Looking down between the trees, they saw a view that would have taken their breath away if they had had any left. All along the winding little river were humpy hills with buildings on them. 'They look like castles in fairy stories,' Nannerl said. Deep down below were the higgledy-piggledy roofs of Salzburg, with the twin towers of the Cathedral and the square opposite the Archbishop's Palace.

'I can see our house!' cried Wolfgang, pointing to a huddle of buildings near the Market. 'I can see Mamma looking out of the window!'

'Wolfgang, don't tell such stories,' his father scolded. 'You couldn't possibly see Mamma from here, unless you had a spy-glass.'

'I can see the Castle!' Nannerl shouted. And so she could, for you couldn't possibly mistake the huge, towering walls to the south of the city.

In between the hills were green fields, and you could see the tiny flocks of sheep and hear cow-bells tinkling when the wind was blowing towards you. And far, far beyond were jagged rows of mountains rising up all round them, and stretching away for ever and ever, it seemed, snow-capped and beautiful in a rather frightening kind of way.

'Over there is Germany,' Leopold said, pointing to his right. 'If you go through those mountains, you come to Munich and to Augsburg, where I was born. One day we will go there and meet all the uncles and aunts and cousins I haven't seen for so long. And behind us – you can't see it, because the mountains are in the way – is the Wolfgang

Lake, and St Gilgen, where Mamma was born. And over there –' Leopold wheeled round and pointed away to the left – 'over there is Italy, where they love music better than anywhere else in the world.'

Switzerland, France, England – he told the children about so many different countries that they became bewildered. And suddenly Wolfgang asked one of those really big questions that fathers never know how to answer.

'Papa,' he asked, 'how big is the world?'

'That's silly,' Nannerl said. 'Nobody knows that.'

'Yes, they do,' Leopold said. 'They know that it's twenty-five thousand miles all the way round. But who can imagine anything as big as that?' He explained to them that Austria was in Europe, and that there was a new continent called America, and that there were parts of Asia and Africa which had never been explored. 'And some people even say,' he went on, 'that there is a huge piece of land to the south of the Pacific Ocean, but nobody has been there yet to find out for certain. Perhaps it's only a sailor's story after all.'

'I want to see the world,' Wolfgang said. 'Can we go and see it tomorrow?'

'Not tomorrow,' Leopold laughed. 'But don't worry, you'll see enough of it some day – more than you want, I expect. For we musicians have to travel, whether we want to or not. We have to earn our living wherever we can.'

Wolfgang jumped up and tugged at his father's arm. 'When can we start seeing the world?' he asked.

'Perhaps sooner than you expect,' Leopold answered quietly. 'Perhaps next year, if you attend to your music lessons and work hard.'

For a plan had been forming in Leopold's mind for several months now. Why shouldn't the Mozart family seek their fortunes somewhere else? Salzburg was a nice little town, but it wasn't a place to seek fame and fortune in. The Archbishop would probably give him leave of absence for a few months. Why not take the children to some of the Royal Courts of Europe? They could give concerts – Nannerl could play the clavier as well as any grown-up musician, and Wolfgang had made astonishing progress lately. By next year he would be ready to give concerts. He would talk things over with Mamma this evening, and see what could be done.

The sun began to sink, and a chilly breeze blew through the trees. 'Time to go home,' Leopold said, 'or Mamma will scold me for keeping you out so late.'

Slowly they began to go down the hillside towards the town. When they got home, Wolfgang was so sleepy that he could hardly eat his supper. His head was full of what Papa had told him about the world.

'I want to go to Italy, and France, and England, and – oh, everywhere!' he kept saying drowsily.

The canary suddenly began to sing. It was a special phrase that he always sang in the evening, round about Wolfgang's bedtime. Wolfgang slipped off his chair at the supper table and went over to the clavier. He picked out the little bit of a tune the canary was singing, and began turning it into a tune of his own.

Papa and Mamma watched him, smiling, for a few moments, and then carried him off to bed, still protesting that he wanted to see the world *tomorrow*. And the canary went on singing and singing.

'The canary is one of us too,' Leopold said, as he blew the candle out. 'He is a musician like us. He must sing for his bread. But he doesn't want to see the world. His cage is big enough for him.'

Wolfgang said nothing; he was fast asleep.

2

On the Road

The young Mozarts, Wolfgang and Nannerl, began to see the world sooner than they ever expected. One crisp September morning, when it was scarcely light, Wolfgang felt himself being lifted out of his bed.

'Wake up, wake up!' cried his mother. 'Get washed and dressed as quick as you can, or you'll miss the coach!'

'Coach?' the little boy yawned, rubbing his eyes. 'What coach? Are we going for a ride in a coach?' He looked sleepily round his candle-lit bedroom. 'But it's the middle of the night!'

'No, it isn't. The sun will be up in half an hour. Hurry, now!'

There were big boxes and trunks all over the floor, carefully roped and labelled by Mamma and Papa, who had been up half the night packing.

'Where are we going, Papa?' asked Nannerl, who was already dressed.

'We're going to Vienna,' Papa said. 'It will take us a week or two, because we are going to stay with friends on the way.'

'Vienna? That's where the Emperor lives,' Wolfgang said. 'Shall we see the Emperor, Papa?'

'Perhaps,' Papa smiled. 'And perhaps not. It all depends.'

'What is the Emperor like?' Wolfgang asked excitedly. 'Has he got a beard? Does he wear his crown all the time, even in bed? Will we have to play for him? Will he have our heads chopped off if we make mistakes?'

'Did you ever hear a boy ask so many questions?' his mother laughed. She sponged his face and neck and hands quickly, and helped him into his tight knee-breeches. 'Now sit down quietly and don't get your clothes dirty before you start. Leopold, dear, are you sure you packed your liver pills? They eat very rich food in Vienna, I've heard, and you never know for certain whether the water's fit to drink.'

Poor Mamma Mozart was rushing about anxiously, worrying about everything. There was really no need to worry, but she was upset because she was not used to travelling, and hated to be away from home. How long would they be gone? Probably two or three months, or even longer. She would miss Salzburg terribly.

'First we are going to Passau, where the Bishop has invited us to stay,' Leopold explained to the children. 'Then we are to give a concert in Linz. We have letters of introduction to several great houses on the way to Vienna, and I expect one of them will put in a good word for us at the Emperor's Court.'

They had a quick breakfast of chocolate and bread, but Wolfgang was too excited to eat much. Then Leopold went out into the street and collected as many men as he could to carry their luggage to the coach, which started from Cathedral Square, several streets away.

At last they were ready to go. The neighbours came crowding round the front door to see them off, and Mamma was afraid she was going to cry. Wolfgang had quite a lump in his throat, too, but the long coach ride was such an adventure that he soon cheered up.

'After all,' Nannerl said bravely, 'it isn't the first time we've been away from home. We'll get used to it, just as we did when we went to Munich last winter.'

'Munich is only seventy-five miles away,' Leopold smiled. 'Vienna is much, much farther!'

The little town of Salzburg looked very beautiful in the early-morning light as the coach crossed the river and began to climb up, up into the mountains that seemed to be closing in all round them. Soon the river valley, with its castles and houses perched on hills, disappeared. The road grew worse and worse, the wheels of the coach scrunched and groaned, the coachman cracked his whip and made strange bellowing noises to his horses.

They stayed the first night in a cold, damp, smelly inn at Braunau where the beds were hard as stones, and the dinner was rather like old boots boiled in glue. Poor Papa's indigestion kept him awake most of the night, but the children were so tired after being bumped about in the coach all day that they slept soundly and had to be shaken hard before they would wake up in the morning. After breakfast Papa told the landlord what he thought of his inn, and they argued for some minutes until the landlord crossly said that he would take fifteen *kreutzer* off the bill.

The coach started off again with fresh horses, and late that afternoon they arrived in Passau. Here was the biggest river Wolfgang had ever seen – the broad, rolling Danube which, Papa said, rose in Switzerland and flowed on and on until it came to the Black Sea, over a thousand miles away. 'You'll see plenty of the Danube before we get to Vienna,' he said.

At the Bishop's Palace everyone was very kind to them. Wolfgang gave several concerts, and the Bishop gave him a golden ducat – the biggest coin he had ever seen in his life. Best of all, and this delighted Papa more than anything, the Bishop paid for their lodgings in the town, which were very homelike and comfortable.

After five days they said goodbye to Passau, and Count Herberstein, a friend of the Bishop's, gave them a lift in his own coach to Linz. Here they stayed in lodgings kept by two funny old maiden ladies called the Misses Kiener, who spoiled the children dreadfully. Count Herberstein introduced them to another friend of his, Count Schlick, who asked the children to give another concert for his friends. By this time Wolfgang and Nannerl were so used to giving concerts that they weren't in the least nervous.

Papa, counting his money, was very satisfied: already the tour was paying its way – and they hadn't even got to Vienna yet! A Bishop and two Counts were interested in the children. No, three Counts – for young Count Palffy, a friend of the first two, was so impressed with Wolfgang and Nannerl that he wrote a special letter to the Court at Vienna, where he was very well known, imploring the Emperor and Empress to hear them play when they came to the capital.

'So it is in life,' Papa said shrewdly. 'Mark my words,

children—never make enemies among people of fashion. Once a great noble likes you, he will tell his friends, and soon *you* will be fashionable, and then suddenly you will be in demand wherever you go.'

From Linz they took the afternoon riverboat—it was the first time the children had ever sailed anywhere—and sailed down the great winding Danube. When night came, they rolled themselves in rugs and slept on the cold hard benches of the cabin as well as they could.

Next day, about noon, they came to a village called Ybbs. They hadn't had a hot meal for twenty-four hours, and Papa decided to get off the boat here and see what they could find in the way of dinner.

There was nowhere to eat except the old monastery. 'It's better than an inn,' Papa explained to the children. 'The monks are not very strict, and they enjoy a good table and a flask of wine.'

Wolfgang was rather frightened of the old, dark building at first. It was so silent, and the monks shuffled about so softly. But they were full of kindness and smiles for the children, and quickly made them feel at home.

It was a strange place for a high-spirited little boy of six to find himself. More than anything in the world, Wolfgang wanted to make a *noise*. To shout or sing or stamp his feet—or just play music, perhaps.

'Papa, they say there is a great organ in the chapel here,' he begged. 'Do you think they would let me play it?'

Mamma thought not, but Papa said, 'H'm. We'll see. Let's go and look at it, anyway.'

They all tiptoed into the chapel, like naughty children raiding a larder, and climbed into the organ loft. It really was a magnificent instrument, Leopold thought, with all the latest stops and pedals. He explained them to the children.

'The keyboard's like a harpsichord,' he said. 'But you must remember to *sustain* the notes by holding them down long enough. Try a note or two, Wolferl, just softly. I'll blow the bellows for you.'

This was exactly what Wolfgang had been waiting for. Papa was going to get the surprise of his life. He had given the boy one or two lessons on the little organ at Maria-Plain Church near Salzburg, where the Mozarts sometimes went on Sundays. What he didn't know was that Wolfgang had been going there once or twice a week with Mamma and practising.

So, instead of the few timid notes he expected, Papa was astonished to hear a Bach Toccata rumbling through the chapel at full strength. He pumped away at the bellows until the sweat dripped from his brow, while Wolfgang's small hands flew like spiders over the manuals.

Suddenly the doors of the chapel were flung open and the Abbot himself appeared. Behind him trooped a procession of monks, one or two of them still wiping their mouths on their napkins, for they were at dinner.

Papa Mozart was so surprised, what with Wolfgang's playing and the monks' interruption, that he stopped pumping. The wind in the pipes made a dismal moaning noise as the music died away.

'That's enough, Wolfgang,' Papa whispered. 'I fear the Abbot is angry with us.'

The monks filed in quietly and seated themselves in the pews. The Abbot's voice came deeply through the chapel. 'Bravo, Herr Mozart! It is not often that we hear music like that. Pray continue – if blowing the bellows is not too tiring for your children.'

'It is not I who am playing, Father,' Papa stammered. 'It is my son, Wolfgang. Please forgive us for disturbing you at dinner.'

'A boy can play the organ like that?' said the Abbot. 'Did you hear, my brothers? It was the boy playing, not the father! But go on, boy! Our dinner can wait.'

So Wolfgang went back to his manuals, and Leopold to his pumping, and the little chapel was filled with music for nearly an hour. Then the monks took the Mozart family off to their refectory for dinner, and made much of the children. Wolfgang never knew that monks could be so jolly, and he was very sorry to leave them next morning when it was time to move on towards Vienna.

For that, Papa explained, was the wandering life of a musician – always making new friends, and having to leave them without knowing whether you will ever see them again.

That evening they arrived at a village called Stein, and slept in a rather dirty lodging house. Mamma was afraid the beds had not been properly aired, and was shocked when she peeped into the kitchen and saw there were cockroaches running about the floor. Poor Mamma! For her nothing was ever as comfortable as her own home.

Next day they were up early again to catch the Vienna boat. It was a rainy, windy day, and they couldn't spend much time on deck or they would have got wet through. Mamma had managed to buy some bread and cheese and apples from an old woman on the landing stage at Stein, and that was enough to keep them going until they went ashore again.

It was about half-past two when the boat rounded a bend in the great wide river – and suddenly, in the distance, was the biggest city Wolfgang had ever seen. A huge forest of rooftops and chimneys and church spires.

Even Papa was impressed. 'Why,' he said, 'you could get forty Salzburgs into Vienna!' For Vienna it was – next to London and Paris, the greatest city in Europe.

B

The boat nosed its way to a quayside, and all passengers for Vienna were told to leave the ship and proceed to the customs office. Wolfgang and Nannerl knew about customs offices; you could hardly travel fifty miles without going through one. The same dreary questions were always asked. 'Have you anything to declare? How much money are you carrying? Where are you going to? What is your business here?' The men who asked the questions were always dreary too, as they wrote down the answers with squeaky quill pens.

There were two men at this particular customs office, a thin, grumpy one with a streaming cold, and a fat cheerful one with a loud hee-hawing laugh.

'Well, and what have we here?' said the fat one, when he saw the Mozarts' music books. 'And what's this – a brace of pistols, eh?' He was turning Leopold's violin case over and over in his podgy hands. 'I shall have to look into this, you know. Very suspicious.' He opened the case and took out the violin.

'Gently, gently, man,' Leopold said crossly. 'It's an Italian instrument, and cost me a great deal of money.'

'Money, eh?' scowled the thin grumpy customs man. 'Atishoo! And how do we know that you really are a musician? For all we know, you may be smuggling foreign violins into Vienna! Atishoo! Or this here instrument –' he shook it hard to see if it rattled – 'may be full of contraband tobacco, or silk, or gold. Atishoo!'

'We are all musicians,' Leopold snapped.

'Surely you can see that, Officer!' Mamma added soothingly.

Suddenly Wolfgang's voice piped up: 'If you don't believe us, sir, we can prove it. Listen!' He seized the violin and began to play a lively dance tune on it.

'Well, I'll be –!' The two customs men stared at him.

'Did you ever hear of such a thing! A kid of his age playing the fiddle like that! Must be a circus dwarf!'

'I can imitate a cat chasing a mouse, too!' cried Wolfgang excitedly. 'Listen!'

He made a fearful miaowing noise by running his finger down the string, and then a series of very high squeaks with the bow very near the bridge of the violin. Even the thin grumpy customs man smiled, and the fat one gave a great bellow of laughter.

'All right, all right,' he said to the thin one. 'Put 'em down as "travelling entertainers". I'll make an exception in your case, Herr Mozart. There'll be nothing to pay this time. Good day to you all. Next, please.'

So the Mozarts came to Vienna, and less than an hour later they were settling down comfortably to a late lunch in their lodgings in the Hierbergasse, a narrow street near the City Park. The food was homely and good, but the beds were far too narrow. Papa had to share one with Wolfgang, and Mamma with Nannerl, and they spent half the night kicking each other out.

Those first few days in Vienna were an anxious time for Papa Mozart. They must give a concert soon, or they would run out of money.

'Phew!' Papa said, as he gloomily examined his purse at the end of each day. 'I knew life in Vienna would be expensive, but I never thought it would be as bad as this! We hire two or three carriages a day to get about the city, and they cost three times as much as carriages in Salzburg!'

'Why don't we walk, Papa?' Nannerl asked. 'It would save so much money.'

'No, no.' Leopold shook his head. 'It would never do to walk. In Vienna you have to keep up appearances. Why, if we walked everywhere, people would think we were too poor to afford a carriage!'

Every morning Wolfgang and Nannerl had to practise their music, and every afternoon Papa gave them lessons in Latin and arithmetic.

'For you cannot go to school like other children,' he explained. 'And I will not have my son and daughter grow up ignorant. So I will teach you myself until we stay long enough in one place for you to go to the local school.'

So there was plenty of hard work in those first few weeks in Vienna.

3

The Little Archduchess

One morning a smart, gold-braided messenger drove up to the Mozarts' lodgings carrying a very large folded piece of paper with the Emperor's seal on it.

'Aha! So we haven't waited in vain!' Papa cried triumphantly. 'Our good friends Count Herberstein and

Count Palffy have spoken for us at Court!' He opened the letter and read it aloud.

Herr Mozart and his two children, it said, were summoned to present themselves at Schönbrunn Palace on October the thirteenth at three o'clock in the afternoon.

Immediately Mamma Mozart flew into one of her panics and sent for a seamstress and a tailor to make a new dress for Nannerl and a new suit for Wolfgang. They all had their wigs curled and powdered, and Papa bought Wolfgang a very grown-up sword to wear with his new suit. Wolfgang liked wearing his sword although he tripped over it sometimes, but the suit was so covered with gold braid and lace and silver buttons that he felt rather silly in it.

'Clothes make the man,' Papa said. 'That's an old proverb, and a wise one. You want to look your best for the young ladies at Court, don't you?'

Papa worked out a concert programme for Wolfgang and Nannerl, and they rehearsed it twice a day.

'We will begin with a concerto by Wagenseil,' he said. 'Herr Wagenseil is the Emperor's Director of Music, and he will be very pleased and surprised to hear you play one of his own compositions. As for you, Nannerl, I want you to practise playing the clavier with the keyboard covered, so that you cannot see your fingers.'

'But why, Papa?' Nannerl asked.

'Oh, it always gets a lot of applause,' Papa said. 'I'm sure I don't know why, for it isn't very difficult. It just _looks_ difficult, like playing cross-hand. And I will write you one or two special arrangements of tunes from Gluck's operas. He's very popular in Vienna now, and it will amuse the Court.'

On the morning of October the thirteenth, Wolfgang nearly drove his poor father mad with questions about the

Empress and the Archduchesses, her daughters, and the Palace. Goodness knows what he thought they were going to be like.

At the last moment Mamma said, 'Leopold, I think I'll stay at home. My dress isn't really good enough for the Court, and anyway I've got a bit of a headache. It's you and the children they really want to see.'

'But, my dear –' Papa protested, but he knew it was in vain. Mamma never thought of herself, she only thought of them. She loved to be at home and she was perfectly happy as long as she got Papa and the children off to their concerts. They would tell her all about it afterwards, and she would share their excitement, and that was all she wanted.

Punctually at half-past two a carriage arrived to take Leopold and the children to Schönbrunn Palace. A small crowd collected outside the inn to see them off; it was very seldom that a coach with the Imperial coat of arms painted on the doors was to be seen in that humble back street, and the proud footman who rode on top of it made a wonderful splash of colour.

Through the city they drove. People in the streets stopped and stared and swept off their hats, probably thinking they were cousins of the Imperial Family on a visit to Vienna. At length they came to a huge arch of stone pillars, and beyond it stood the biggest house the Mozarts had ever seen – much, much bigger than the Archbishop's palace in Salzburg. Behind it, an enormous park stretched away as far as they could see, with avenues of tall trees and lakes full of water-lilies and statues of gods and goddesses and little cherubs everywhere.

The carriage pulled up at a small side door, and the Mozarts were shown into a rather stuffy little room and asked to get ready for their concert.

'Their Imperial Majesties will send for you in a few minutes,' said a tall, very dignified man, who was known as the Major-Domo. He disappeared through a gilt door.

'That reminds me,' Papa Mozart told the children, 'don't forget to say "Imperial Majesty" when you speak to the Emperor and Empress, and don't speak at all until you have been spoken to. If the Empress offers you her hand, don't shake it – kiss it very respectfully. And you, Nannerl, curtsey three times to the audience when you have finished playing. Wolfgang, mind you don't talk too much – you know how your tongue runs away with you. Remember, a deep bow when you enter and leave the room, and never turn your back on Royalty – either of you.'

The gilt door opened again and the Major-Domo re-appeared. 'Are you ready, Herr Mozart? Then let us go to the music room.'

They were led through long passages lined with statues and suits of armour to a huge pair of doors guarded by two footmen standing stiffly to attention. The doors opened and the Major-Domo called out in a deep voice: 'Herr Leopold Mozart and his two children.'

They went into a room much smaller than they had expected, and bowed deeply. Wolfgang kept his head down so long that he had no idea who else was in the room. At last he heard Papa talking, and timidly raised his eyes.

The richly-carved furniture, the curtains, the golden mirrors, the glittering candelabra, the highly-polished floor in which you could see your own face reflected – he had never seen anything like it before. There were about twenty people in the room. He at once recognized the Empress Maria Theresa because he had seen her face on coins. She was smiling kindly towards him. The stout gentleman sitting next to her must be Emperor Francis I.

But they weren't wearing robes and crowns. In fact they looked just like ordinary people, except that their clothes were the finest he had ever seen.

There were children, too. 'And this is the Archduchess Joanna and Archduchess Marie-Antoinette,' someone was saying. Wolfgang bowed again, and then had a good look at the little girl who was called Marie-Antoinette, and who seemed to be about his own age. Could this be an Archduchess? She was very pretty, too.

'Good afternoon, boy,' she said rather disdainfully. 'How do you do?'

'I'm – I'm very well, thank you,' Wolfgang stammered. He bowed again, and nearly fell over his sword. The little Archduchess giggled, and Wolfgang decided that he liked her after all.

Now Papa was talking to Herr Wagenseil, the Emperor's Director of Music. Could this be the composer of the concerto he had been practising so hard for several weeks? They were looking through the big books of music Papa had brought under his arm.

'Come, Herr Mozart,' said the Emperor in a friendly voice. 'Let us hear these remarkable young musicians we have heard so much about.'

Nannerl played the clavier first, a difficult Italian piece, with so many notes that Wolfgang was terrified she was going to make a mistake. But she didn't, and as she came to the last chords, everybody cried 'Bravo!' and clapped loudly. Nannerl gave her three curtseys, and the Empress made room for her to sit on a hassock at her feet.

'Now let us see what the young gentleman with the sword can do!' said the Emperor, his eyes twinkling. 'What are you going to play for us, my boy?'

'Please, I'd like to play a concerto by Herr Wagenseil,' said Wolfgang. 'Papa, I hope you haven't lost the music?'

Everybody laughed, and Wolfgang felt relieved. Why, they weren't as stuffy as Papa seemed to think. They obviously found him amusing, just as the customs men had done. Should he do his imitation of the cat and the mouse on the violin, and make them laugh still more? But Papa was tuning the violin now – they were to play this piece together.

Herr Wagenseil seemed delighted and lifted Wolfgang on to the music stool.

'Don't go away, Herr Wagenseil,' the boy said. 'You must turn the pages for me, otherwise I shall get in a muddle. Stand here beside me, please.'

'Wolfgang!' His father was horrified. 'You must not talk to Herr Wagenseil like that. It is most kind of him to –'

'Never mind, Herr Mozart!' the famous composer laughed. 'This boy will go far! Now, shall we begin?'

Wolfgang's face suddenly became serious, as it always did when he was playing or listening to music. His eyes were fixed on his father, waiting for the signal to begin.

The music was fast and bold at first, followed by a gentle, thoughtful melody. Then the two tunes were cleverly mixed together, and suddenly became something quite different, until the first tune came back again in another key.

A faraway look came into the Emperor's eyes. The Empress beat time with one hand. Herr Wagenseil, turning the pages, caught Papa Mozart's eye for a moment and smiled; it was easy to see how pleased he was. At last the concerto was over, and everyone sighed and then broke into such a storm of applause as the Mozarts had never heard before.

The Empress sent for sweets and cakes and wine. 'The children must be tired and thirsty,' she said. The Emperor walked over to the clavier, put his arm round Wolfgang's shoulders and said, 'The boy is a magician. I cannot believe that it was he playing – and yet I must believe my own eyes!'

'If it please your Imperial Majesty,' Papa Mozart said proudly, 'my children can do many other things besides. My son will improvise on any tune you care to name, and my daughter can play with the keyboard covered – indeed, they both can.'

And so it went on all afternoon, until at last the Empress said, 'See, the sun is shining. It's not good for children to stay indoors too much. If your son and daughter would care to see the Palace and the Gardens, Herr Mozart, my children will be pleased to show their guests round.'

'Your Imperial Majesty is too kind,' said Papa Mozart. He whispered to Wolfgang, 'Say thank you, and kiss the Empress's hand!'

'Oh, thank you, Imperial Majesty!' Wolfgang gasped. 'I should love to see your garden! Has it got flowers in it, and do you grow potatoes?' He ran forward and, standing on tiptoe, kissed the Empress's cheek. Papa Mozart cried, 'Wolfgang! What did I tell you?'

But the Empress didn't mind at all. 'He is a charming boy,' she laughed. 'And he will charm many ladies when he is older!'

The Archduchess Joanna took charge of Nannerl. Little Marie-Antoinette said, 'Come along, boy. We will go into the Gardens.'

Wolfgang ran forward to take her hand, but what with his new shoes and the polished floor, his legs suddenly shot from under him and he slipped and fell with a crash. He felt terribly foolish.

'Poor boy,' said the little Archduchess, as she helped him to his feet and brushed his suit down for him. 'I hope you didn't hurt yourself?'

'It was nothing,' said Wolfgang, awkwardly rubbing his behind, which really was rather painful. 'You are very kind to me,' he said seriously, 'and very beautiful too. I think I shall marry you when I grow up.'

There was more laughter. 'What did I tell you?' cried the Empress. 'Did I not say he was a ladies' man?'

Papa stayed behind to talk to the Emperor and Empress and Herr Wagenseil, and the children went through more long passages and huge rooms until at last Wolfgang saw the sunshine streaming in through the glass doors. They went through the doors into the biggest garden he had ever seen. You simply could not see the end of it; it seemed to stretch away into the distance for ever and ever. There were long avenues of trees, lakes, lily ponds, statues of gods and goddesses, big stone flower-bowls with plants growing in them, and the most wonderful fresh smell of flowers everywhere.

They walked on and on, Wolfgang asking hundreds of questions, until he suddenly noticed that he was alone with the Archduchess Marie-Antoinette. 'We have lost Nannerl and your sister,' he said anxiously. 'Shouldn't we look for them?'

'Don't be silly, boy,' the little Archduchess said. 'My sister knows her way back to the Palace. We live here. We play in the Gardens every day. How old are you, boy?'

'I'm six and three-quarters. How old are you?'

'You shouldn't ask a lady her age. It's rude,' she said.

'I'm sorry,' Wolfgang said, confused. Then he decided that she was just making fun of him. 'I don't really want to know how old you are.'

'I'm nearly seven,' she said. 'I'm older than you. And much taller.'

Wolfgang knew he was small for his age, and hated people to refer to it. 'Girls grow faster than boys,' he said.

'Papa says so. It's not my fault that I'm not as tall as you.'

'Can you run races?' Marie-Antoinette asked.

'I don't know. I've never tried.'

She pointed to a big statue of a Greek goddess about two hundred yards away. 'I'll race you to there. Are you ready? One, two, three, GO!'

She was off, picking up her skirts and petticoats, almost before Wolfgang was ready. He dashed after her, puffing and panting, as fast as his thin little legs could carry him, but she was at the archway several seconds before him.

'You run very well,' he gasped. It really was awful, being beaten by a girl.

'Take your coat off, boy,' she laughed. 'You'll run much better. That's it. Now back to where we started from. One, two, three, GO!'

This time Wolfgang did much better, but she was still a yard or two ahead of him.

'You're just letting me win,' she panted. 'Try really hard next time. After all, you don't have to wear these silly skirts! One, two, three, GO!'

They arrived at the archway at the very same moment, and immediately began quarrelling about who had won.

'I touched this pillar,' Marie-Antoinette cried. 'You have to touch the curving part with your hand. It's one of the rules!'

'It isn't,' Wolfgang said indignantly. 'Or, if it is, you should have told me at the beginning!'

'Pooh! Everyone knows that you have to touch the winning post.'

'Horses don't have to in horse racing,' he said.

'We're not horses,' she argued.

'Anyway, it's all very well for you,' he said crossly. 'You can run races every day. I have to stay at home practising my music. And it's very hard work, I can tell you!'

'You and your music!' Her eyes flashed. 'Do you think nobody else plays the clavier? I have music lessons too, and my Mamma sings beautifully, and so does my sister. A boy ought to be able to run races as well as play music!'

'I think you're being horrid to me!' he burst out.

'Wolfgang Mozart!' Her voice was suddenly sharp. 'You mustn't speak to me like that. I am of Royal blood, and you are only a musician.'

'*Only* a musician?' He could hardly believe his ears. 'But music is the most wonderful thing in the world. Papa says we should be proud of being musicians!'

'Be proud if you like.' The little Archduchess tossed her head. 'But you must not be disrespectful. You may kiss my hand.'

The little girl, half a head taller than Wolfgang, looked very proud and beautiful. 'I'm sorry,' he said awkwardly. 'I didn't understand.' He bowed over the small white hand she offered him, and kissed it.

'I'm sorry, too,' she said softly. 'You were right, Wolfgang Mozart. I *was* being horrid to you. Let's not quarrel any more.'

They walked back towards the Palace. Wolfgang was very thoughtful. For a few moments this little girl had spoken to him as if he were a servant, a clumsy footman who had dropped a glass vase and broken it. She had seemed a little girl like any other little girl in Salzburg, except for her fine clothes. Of course, she *was* the Emperor's daughter. She was an Archduchess. Somehow he had imagined an Archduchess as a sort of old Ugly Sister in a fairy tale, not a little girl who would run races with him in a big park that was her own private playground. It was all very confusing.

They returned to the music room, where Papa was thanking everybody for being so kind to the children.

They said goodbye to everybody, and bowed and kissed many hands, and then got into the coach that was to take them back to their lodgings.

Mamma had a hot supper ready for them. She had quite got rid of her headache, she said. She was in very good spirits and longing to hear all about their adventures at Schönbrunn. Papa showed the children the presents the Emperor and Empress and their friends had given them.

'Here's a gold snuffbox for you, Wolfgang, and a gold toothpick too. And a brooch and a diamond ring for Nannerl. And for Mamma and me –' he tapped a leather bag – 'enough money to see us through the winter.' He sighed. 'It is good to have jewels and trinkets; their value does not change in different countries. But what poor musicians need is money, paid regularly. These fine ladies and gentlemen don't understand that.'

He went on to tell them about his plans for the rest of their time in Vienna. 'We are to play at the Countess Kinsky's next month, and Herr Wagenseil will give me letters to many other houses in the city. And – I nearly forgot to tell you! – the Empress has ordered her own dressmaker to call on us and make a Court dress for you, Nannerl – just like the ones the Court ladies wear – and a fine velvet suit for you, Wolfgang. You will wear them at all our concerts in future, so that everyone will know that we have played before the Emperor and Empress!'

'Will we see the Archduchesses again, Papa?' asked Nannerl.

'I don't know,' Papa said. 'I expect so, if we are invited to the Palace again.'

'Do you think I *could* marry Marie-Antoinette when I grow up?' asked Wolfgang seriously. 'Of course, she's older than I am, and I suppose it's rather awkward having a wife who's taller than yourself.'

'What an idea!' Papa Mozart laughed. 'Why, she will marry someone of her own kind! A Prince, or even a King. Archduchesses can't marry just whom they please, you know. They certainly can't marry poor musicians. No, a musician, too, should marry someone of his own kind – perhaps the daughter of another musician. Someone who understands music, and can help him in his work.'

'I see, Papa,' said Wolfgang. But he didn't really see. And for many years afterwards he remembered the little Archduchess who had helped him to his feet when he slipped on the floor of the Palace, and who had played with him in the great park of Schönbrunn.

And when at last they all went home to Salzburg, and talked about their adventures in Vienna, he used to make them laugh by boasting, 'One day I shall be very rich and famous, and I shall be an Archduke, and I shall go to Vienna and say: "Marie-Antoinette, you may be an Arch-duchess, and you may be able to run faster than I can, but I am Wolfgang Amadeus Mozart of Salzburg, and you could do a lot worse than marry me!"'

4

Paris and Pompadour

The coach and four roared and rattled over the cobbles as it climbed the hill out of Mons. Wolfgang Mozart, his nose pressed to the window as he sat on Papa's knees,

took a last look at the little Belgian village in the frosty
November dawn.

And half an hour later, Papa rubbed the mist from the
window and said, 'Now we're in France.'

'It doesn't look very different from Belgium,' Nannerl
said.

'It will soon,' Papa said. 'Here in the north it's much
flatter than in Austria. You won't see any mountains with
snow on them. You'll be lucky if you see any snow at all,
for all it's November.'

Mamma, huddled in a corner, was feeling the cold.

'I'm afraid it's a rough life for you, my dear.' Papa
smiled comfortingly. 'Look at the way we musicians live!
We've visited twelve cities in four months. Some great
people were kind enough to hear the children play, and
others either weren't at home or said they hadn't time.
Well, that's the luck of the game.'

'How far is it to Paris, Papa?' Wolfgang asked.

'Oh, a good two days more,' Papa replied.

'Two days!' the boy groaned. 'How on earth shall we
pass the time till then?'

'Well, I could hear your Latin irregular verbs,' said
Papa solemnly, knowing that there was nothing Wolfgang hated more. 'It's long enough since you had any
schooling. Or how about a bit of arithmetic? Of course,
we can always play "Find the Tune".'

This was a family game of the Mozarts when on long
journeys. One of them would hum a bit of a Haydn quartet
or a Bach fugue, or an aria from a Gluck opera, and the
others would have to say where it came from. Sometimes,
to make it harder, Papa would hum the 'cello part alone,
so that they would have to find the tune that went on top
of it; and sometimes he would turn the tune upside down.

'It's no use playing "Find the Tune",' Nannerl said.

'Wolfgang always wins. I wish this coach didn't shake so much; I'd like to read.'

Mamma was looking a little sad. She was very homesick for Salzburg. She hated moving on to a fresh place every week or so. What was the use of having a home, and taking so much trouble to make it clean and pretty and comfortable, if you were away from it so much?

'I do hope you're right, Leopold,' she sighed to her husband. 'I sometimes wonder if you haven't spoilt your chance with the Archbishop by coming on this tour.'

'Pooh! It's very kind of His Grace to make me Deputy Director of Music, when he must know I am fully qualified to be Director,' Leopold said impatiently. 'I cannot wait all my life for promotion. When a man is in his forties, as I am, he is at his best. He has experience and plenty of energy for making use of it.'

Mamma glanced at the two children, who were looking out of the window and chattering to themselves. They weren't listening to what their parents were saying, and it was just as well.

'But the Archbishop might have made you Director, Leopold, if you weren't away from Salzburg so much. He's a generous man, but you can't expect him to pay you for never being there when he needs you!'

'He doesn't need me,' Leopold replied. 'Michael Haydn is a good fellow and a fine musician – not as good as his elder brother Joseph, of course, but sound and practical. He'll make a good Director of Music. And there are plenty of other musicians about the Court. Anyway, that isn't the point. The point is that we have Wolfgang and Nannerl. Wolfgang, I have not the smallest doubt, is a genius.'

'A genius!' she whispered. 'How can you be sure?'

'I am very sure,' he said. 'No other boy in the world has ever learned to play the violin in a few days as he did. No other boy ever wrote music when he was only five years old. No other boy ever played a pedal organ at first sight, as he did in Wasserburg a couple of months ago. My dear' – he took his wife's hand tenderly – 'you know I am not a gambler. But for Wolfgang we have to make sacrifices and take big risks.' He smiled. 'Cheer up! We are in France, and we are going to see Paris, the most elegant city in the world!'

'I would rather be at home in Salzburg,' she sighed. 'Or at least, I wish we could stay for a few weeks in one place so that I could get used to it. I was beginning to get quite fond of Brussels, though it isn't nearly as clean as Salzburg.'

'Well, my dear, we'll be home again some time next year – heaven knows when. The longer we stay away, the more money we'll earn! You know how much you want to have a house of your own.'

'Yes,' she murmured, smiling. 'A house like the one I was born in at St Gilgen, looking out on to a lake, with mountains in the background!'

'And Wolfgang said he wanted to see the world! Didn't you, Wolferl? That afternoon we walked up the Kapuzinerberg, eh?'

'I have seen Vienna and Munich and Augsburg and Mannheim and Brussels and–' Wolfgang chanted as he counted on his fingers. 'And all we ever do is play music and bow to the audience and ride in coaches! Perhaps we could go to Siberia one day, Papa, where it would be so cold that our fingers would drop off and then we wouldn't have to play!'

'Siberia? You'd have an audience of Russian bears who would much rather eat you than listen to you playing!' Papa laughed. 'Let's hope the fair ladies of Paris won't eat you up!'

The coach rumbled on through flat green pastures and lovely farms and forest lands and little villages until, at last, they came to Péronne, a village on the banks of the River Somme, where they spent the night at an inn. Here there was a letter waiting for Papa.

'It's from our old friend Baron Grimm,' he said. 'He knows Paris like the back of his hand. He has found rooms for us at the Hotel Beauvais.' Papa looked closely at the letter as if he couldn't believe his eyes. 'Well, this is indeed good news! His excellency the Bavarian Ambassador invites us to stay at his expense! No doubt he thinks it will be good for trade between France and Austria to have the Mozarts giving concerts in his friends' drawing rooms!'

'You see, Leopold, how good it is to be well known at the Archbishop's Court!' Mamma said quietly. 'Count Arco, the Archbishop's Chamberlain, is the Ambassador's father-in-law. I am sure he put in a word for us!'

'Oh, I am grateful enough,' said Leopold. 'Especially when it saves me money! Grimm is really a splendid fellow. He says we are to go and see him as soon as we arrive in Paris, and he will introduce us to all the right people, and perhaps to the King and Queen as well!'

'We are certainly doing things in style this time!' Mamma said. 'It makes such a difference, having our own manservant to help instead of having to tip dozens of rogues to lift our luggage down and tell us the way and find good inns to stay in! Really, I don't know what we should do without Sebastian.'

Sebastian Winter was, at that moment, curled up in the hayloft above the stables, shivering with the night cold and trying in vain to sleep. He was a thin, wiry young man, neatly dressed, and honest as the day was long. However wicked a city Paris was – and they had heard it was full of thieves and swindlers ready to pounce on unwary foreigners – they felt they would be safe in Sebastian's hands.

In the morning they were off again, the coachman whipping up his horses until they fairly flew across the flat meadowlands dotted with little farms.

'They have better roads in France than many we've been travelling on lately,' Papa said. 'Why, this one is like the Ring in Vienna, it's so smooth! We've over eighty miles to go today, and the coachman reckons he can get us there in daylight!'

The coachman was not far wrong. Mist was gathering and dusk was falling when, after driving hard all day with several changes of horses, they rumbled through the suburbs of Paris, and Papa's watch said six o'clock.

The city was in darkness when they arrived at the Hotel Beauvais. Only the coachman's flare and the hotel porter's lantern gave any light, and the Mozarts could see nothing of the city at all, except a few chinks of candlelight through the drawn curtains.

Wearily they followed a footman upstairs. He flung open a door and bowed them into a pleasantly furnished room. Another door led out of it into a bedroom with four beds.

'What in Heaven's name is this?' cried Leopold. 'Is the whole family to sleep in one room?'

'Those are my orders, sir,' said the footman.

'And what about Winter, my servant?'

'He will sleep and eat with the grooms, sir. I am afraid there is a shortage of accommodation in Paris.'

'But his Excellency the Ambassador surely cannot mean –' Leopold began. The footman shrugged and went away.

'It really is too bad,' Leopold fumed. 'Anyone would think we were cattle in the market.'

'Hush, dear,' Mamma said mildly. 'It won't be so bad. We mustn't expect things to be as comfortable as they are at home. After all, we are the Ambassador's guests, and this really is quite a pretty room.'

After a good meal they all felt much better and went to bed early, sleeping as soundly as they had ever slept in their lives.

Next morning Wolfgang was out of bed before the others, and rushed to the window to see Paris. Actually he couldn't see much of it. The Hotel Beauvais was an elegant house in a narrow street. He saw well-dressed servants walking up and down, and there was a splendid smell of fried onions coming from downstairs. Farther along the street there was a great deal of shouting, and Wolfgang could just see the stalls of a market. Every so often a cart came by, drawn by a tired old horse, and in it were wretched-looking people, dirty and half-starved, who drew jeers and boos from bystanders and people leaning out of the windows.

Wolfgang ran and woke up his father. 'Papa, who are those people in the carts?' he asked.

Papa went sleepily to the window. 'Oh, they are being taken to the Bastille. Probably they have stolen a few coins or a chicken to eat, or can't pay their debts.'

'What is the Bastille, Papa?'

'It's a huge fortress of a prison not far from here. Poor wretches—they are hungry, that is why they steal.' He peered out of the window. 'They don't keep the streets as clean as they do in Salzburg,' he remarked. 'And did you ever see so many loafers begging a coin from everyone who passes by! Look at them!'

After breakfast, Papa's friend Baron Grimm called to see them.

'Why, Herr Baron, I hardly recognised you!' Leopold cried. 'You are the complete Frenchman, I declare!'

'You think so?' said Herr Grimm carelessly. He had a way of holding his snuffbox with his little finger stretched out, and a trick of playing with his lace handkerchief that made Wolfgang want to giggle. 'Well, you know, I have been living here for fifteen years. When in France you have to be French, or you don't get anywhere in society.'

'You think we ought to behave differently, Herr Baron?' Mamma asked anxiously.

'Well –' Herr Grimm looked them up and down critically. 'If you'll excuse my saying so, your clothes are far too German. German music is very fashionable here as you will discover, but not German clothes. This young man, for instance –' he held Wolfgang at arm's length – 'he needs a *black* suit and a French hat. Black is very fashionable, you know, for the Court is in mourning for poor little Princess Isabella, the King's granddaughter, who died of a fever the other day.'

'Oh, dear!' Mamma sighed. 'More expense!'

'Well, if it must be, it must be,' said Papa. 'Clothes make the man, I have always said so. But we must earn some money as soon as possible, or we shall be in debt. I have several letters of introduction to great houses in Paris, Herr Baron. Perhaps you would be so kind as to support them with your personal recommendation, since you know everyone in Paris.'

'I will do my best, of course,' said Herr Grimm. 'But everything here goes at a snail's pace. There is so much etiquette, so much to learn about manners and the right way of doing things.'

'And the Court of Versailles?' Papa asked eagerly. 'We shall be terribly disappointed if we cannot play before the King and Queen.'

Herr Grimm rolled his eyes upwards in despair. 'Oh, my dear friend, you are in too much of a hurry! At Ver-

sailles things go even slower. There are so many hangers-
on and officials, and some of them, let me tell you, are
not above a little bribery! For at Versailles all the nobles
and their servants live above their means, and gamble, and
compete with one another in extravagance, and often they
have hardly a penny in their pockets.'

'But I have been told there is so much wealth and luxury
in France!' Papa said in astonishment.

'Oh, dear me, no!' laughed Herr Grimm. 'The really
rich people are the tradesmen, who save their money to
build big villas in the suburbs, or the prosperous farmers
and landowners who wisely stay in the country and never
come to Court! Why, you cannot be a noble or live at
Versailles at all unless you can trace your family back to
the year 1400!'

'So you think there is no chance of our playing for the
Royal Family?' Leopold asked, crestfallen.

'Oh, I wouldn't say that.' The Baron put his head on
one side and looked rather cunning. 'We will see what can
be done. Meanwhile, I think we should try Madame de
Pompadour.'

Leopold's eyes lit up with new hope. 'Ah, the world has
heard much of Madame Pompadour! Tell me, what is she
really like? I doubt whether *she* can trace her family back
to 1400, eh?'

Baron Grimm burst out laughing. 'No, indeed! She
was born Mademoiselle Poisson – Miss Fish! And they
have had to find a special title for her – Marquise of Pompadour! She rules the Court, right enough. She has fifty-
eight servants – many more than the Queen. She has her
own private theatre, a special house in the park, and I
don't know what else. Some people hate her, others love
her. I'll say this for her – she is kind and generous to
artists, writers and musicians. She even receives them at

Court! Why, she has even made friends with wild fellows like Voltaire and Diderot, who write against the Government, and say we ought to be ruled by a House of Commons, like England!'

'But isn't that treason?' Leopold looked rather shocked.

'Oh, they are just ideas,' Baron Grimm smiled. 'The French are great talkers, you know.'

When the Baron had gone, Papa sat down with quill and ink, and wrote letters to several important people to whom his friends in Salzburg and Vienna and Brussels had given him introductions. They were very polite letters, full of long respectful phrases, such as 'Most honourable and distinguished Monsieur this and that', 'If it please your most worthy Excellency' and 'your most humble and dutiful and obedient servant'. Wolfgang, looking over his shoulder, could make out a few words here and there, and asked, 'But why don't you just *ask* for what you want, instead of writing all those funny words?' Papa told him to run away. It was something he would understand when he was older.

Then they all went out for a carriage ride to look at Paris. It was a strange mixture of beautiful old buildings, spacious squares, parks, and some higgledy-piggledy streets, so dirty and crowded that the smell was dreadful.

'The way people throw their rubbish in the streets!' Leopold cried, muffling his nose in his handkerchief. 'And the mud everywhere! Upon my soul, this would never be allowed in Salzburg!'

Sometimes the traffic was so heavy — coaches and carts, phaetons and sedan chairs all crushed together in narrow streets — that they would be held up for half an hour at a time, while drivers bawled insults at each other, and horses squealed and reared up on their hind legs with fright. The

Mozarts had never seen anything like this – even in Vienna.

After about a week, Papa began to get anxious. Some of the noble lords he had written to had not answered. Others replied saying they were sorry, but they simply hadn't time to receive the Mozart family. Ambassador van Eyck, who had invited them, sent them a message saying they must be patient; meanwhile they could use his music room and his clavier to practise on.

Papa filled in the time by giving Wolfgang special lessons in composition, and Wolfgang sat down cheerfully, with the family talking all round him, and wrote one or two sonatas and some minuets which Papa said weren't too bad for a boy of seven.

'Actually, they are astonishingly good, with a few corrections here and there,' he told Mamma privately. 'But I don't want the boy to get too conceited.'

After about ten days, Baron Grimm came to see them again, looking extremely pleased with himself. 'I've done it!' he said. 'I spoke to a friend who knows someone who knows one of the Court entertainment managers, and there may be a chance of your playing at Versailles after Christmas!'

'After Christmas!' Leopold groaned. 'But that's nearly three weeks away! How are we to live till then?'

'Wait, I have more news for you. The Pompadour has heard of your children, and is curious to see them. You are to take them to Versailles the day after tomorrow. What is more, she will pay your coach-fare!'

As Versailles was a good twelve miles from Paris, Leopold was greatly relieved to hear this.

'Mark my words,' the Baron went on, 'if the Pompadour likes you, you're *in*! You'll become fashionable overnight and you'll be invited everywhere!'

'My good old friend, I am truly grateful to you!' Leopold seized Baron Grimm's hand and shook it warmly.

So they all set out for Versailles in their new clothes, highly excited, with Herr Grimm pointing out all the sights on the way.

At last they came to Versailles village, and the coach rolled and lurched through the mud up the broadest avenue they had ever seen. But what took their breath right away was the most enormous building in the world, or so it seemed. It was so wide that you couldn't see the ends of it.

'The front of it is a quarter of a mile long,' said the Baron. 'And there's still more of it behind. It has thousands of rooms – and two hundred and fifty bathrooms! You could get a dozen Schönbrunn Palaces into it! Wait till you've seen the Hall of Mirrors, lit up by eight thousand candles! The masked balls, the banquets, the fireworks, the gambling that goes on . . . Mind you, the King has other palaces, too – Fontainebleau, Compiègne, and so on – some he only uses for hunting . . .'

'You seem to admire all this luxury, Baron Grimm!' Leopold said sternly. 'I thought you were supposed to be a bit of a revolutionary!'

'Oh well, of course, I don't approve of it. It's all very extravagant and wasteful. Still, you must admit, Herr Mozart, there's nothing else in the whole world like it!'

But Leopold Mozart wasn't listening. He was looking in horror out of the carriage window. Beggars were crawling towards the coach on their hands and knees, crying for coins, food, gifts, anything. Some had only one leg; others had no legs at all.

'Poor wretches,' Baron Grimm said. 'They probably lost their legs in the war, when all Europe tried to steal pieces of our dear Empress Maria Theresa's empire! What a shocking affair that was.'

'But does nobody do anything for them?' asked Leopold. 'Look, there's a woman with a baby among them!' Impulsively he leaned out of the window and threw all the coins he had in his pocket to her. The beggars snarled like wolves and began fighting each other in the mud for a share of the money. Some were so thin and weak from hunger that they were easily shoved aside by the younger and stronger ones.

'To think that there are people in that Palace who have no appetite for their dinner because they ate too much at lunch!' Leopold said. 'And out here, crawling in the mud, are other people who would be happy with a crust! This couldn't happen in Vienna, I'll swear!'

'The King is well aware of the poverty in France,' Grimm said. 'But what can he do? If you shared out all the food in the Palace, there still wouldn't be enough to go round among the poor. Voltaire and Rousseau and their friends are right. We need a new kind of government.'

Now they were rattling through the huge gates of the Palace, the horses' hooves ringing and throwing up sparks on the cobble-stones. The coach was taken round to a side entrance, where it stopped. The Mozarts and Baron Grimm were shown into a small waiting-room.

'The Marquise de Pompadour will send for you when she is ready to receive you,' they were told by a disdainful servant whose periwig was so full of powder that there was a white smear of it on the shoulders of his coat.

5

Christmas at Versailles

The Marquise de Pompadour was not ready to receive
them for a very long time. It must have been an hour or
more before the servant returned and showed them into
a suite of rooms about a hundred yards farther along the
building. Baron Grimm here took his leave. 'The Marquise
does not want *me*,' he smiled. 'It's you she's interested in!

Now don't be frightened of her. Let me know how you get on. I'll be waiting here when you come back.'

The Mozarts, Leopold clutching his violin and portfolio of music, found themselves in a drawing room with a clavier in it. There was more waiting, until at last two footmen opened the doors, turned, and bowed to four ladies who followed them in. The four ladies also turned and curtsied to a fifth lady. All of them wore the fullest dresses with the most elaborate skirts the Mozarts had ever seen, and the tallest wigs too. Their faces were painted like masks, so that you could hardly tell what they were really like underneath. They sailed in and seated themselves. The fifth and last remained standing for a moment or two.

Mamma Mozart curtsied and Papa bowed deeply.

'Herr Mozart?' the fifth lady asked, taking the most comfortable chair of all.

'Madame la Marquise,' Papa murmured. 'You were kind enough to ask to see my children, and perhaps to hear them play.'

'We have heard much of your children, Herr Mozart. It is not easy to believe that children so young—especially your son—can make such music as has been reported to us. But we are always ready to try new sensations, new amusements. Let them perform.'

'If it please your Ladyship, my children will play a movement of a sonata by Joseph Haydn, followed by a set of minuets composed by my son, Wolfgang, and played by him on the clavier.'

'Good. We are tired of French and Italian music, and would like to hear German music for a change.'

Nannerl began to play. Then Wolfgang followed, both on clavier and violin; and then all three, Papa, Nannerl and Wolfgang, played a special arrangement by Papa, for clavier and two violins, of an old French folksong. The ladies applauded rapturously, and Wolfgang gave them several encores by going through his parlour tricks—playing the clavier with the keyboard covered, improvising new tunes with his left hand in perfect harmony with another tune played by his right hand, learning new tunes from the ladies and instantly turning them into variations of his own.

When it was all over, and the clapping and the cries of wonder had died down, the Marquise de Pompadour said to Wolfgang, 'Come here, boy, and let me look at you.'

Wolfgang trotted obediently up to her.

'My eyesight is not as good as it was, and you are very small, young man. Stand on this chair where I can see you.'

The little boy, with his wig and sword and embroidered Court suit, did as he was told. The Marquise inspected him carefully through her lorgnettes. 'Hm. He looks an ordinary enough boy to me. Well, I expect you'd like a present. What should it be, I wonder?'

'I would like to kiss you, pretty Madame,' said Wolfgang.

The other ladies giggled, but soon became silent when they saw the frown on the Pompadour's face.

'You are a very impudent boy,' she snapped. 'I shall certainly not kiss you.'

'Wolfgang!' Papa whispered. 'Apologise at once!'

'I don't see why I should,' the boy said, not at all perturbed. 'Her Majesty, the Empress in Vienna, rewarded me with a kiss when I played for her, and I don't see why this lady shouldn't do the same. After all she is not an Empress. Are you, Madame?'

The other ladies crowded round and kissed both the children and gave them sweets, but the Pompadour just looked haughty and said nothing.

Finally she said, 'Thank you, Herr Mozart. We have

greatly enjoyed your children's music. We will mention them to the King, who may, perhaps, be pleased to send for you again.'

So saying, she gathered up her enormous skirts and, with her four ladies, swept out of the room.

'Well!' Papa said to Mamma. 'So that's the great Pompadour! One of the sights of France, like Notre Dame Cathedral! What will the Hagenauers say when we write home to Salzburg and tell them we have met and talked with the Pompadour?'

'And that she was absolutely horrid to Wolfgang,' Mamma said indignantly.

'Poor little chap,' Papa said. 'He meant no harm.'

'She is still beautiful,' said Mamma, 'though she must be at least forty.'

'I can think of one other woman,' Papa smiled at Mamma, 'who surpasses her at that age!'

'At least I don't paint my face like that,' Mamma said.

'You don't have to, my dear!' Papa said gallantly. 'But really, have you ever seen such painted women in your life as in this Palace? Every time I look out of the window I see more of them. Why, if Austrian women behaved like that, we would drive them out of town!'

'They remind me of Berchtesgaden dolls!' Mamma laughed. She meant those little wooden figures made by peasants in Austrian and German villages, with bright spots of red on the cheeks and lips, and black-painted eyes.

They made their way out on to the terrace behind the Palace, where the Swiss Guards strutted up and down with enormous pikes, and stood rooted to the spot with sheer astonishment. If the gardens of Schönbrunn had seemed huge, the ones they saw now were vast beyond comparison. They seemed to go on for ever and ever. There was a cross-shaped lake which seemed to be a mile long, and avenues

c

that criss-crossed each other like trellis work. There were
fountains playing everywhere, woods, streams and bridges,
and sometimes houses; and every few yards were statues
on pedestals – hundreds of them, it seemed – statues of
Roman gods and goddesses, imitations of classical Greek
sculptures. Everything you looked at, in every direction,
seemed to disappear into the horizon.

Wolfgang and Nannerl were delighted with it all,
especially with the fountains, but Papa kept thinking of the
beggars he had seen outside the Palace. 'It cannot go on
like this,' he muttered to himself. 'Soon, something must
blow up. And when that happens, heaven help France!'

Baron Grimm, who took them home in his coach, did
not agree. 'It is simply a question of changing people's
ideas, of educating the masses. One day the people will
say to the King, "Good morning, Your Majesty, the time
has come for you to go." And a People's Government will
be set up, and we shall all be brothers in equality! Think
how glorious that will be!'

But Leopold shook his head uneasily. 'I do not think
so. When people are really hungry, there is always
bloodshed.'

The Mozarts waited patiently for another week or so,
wondering whether Wolfgang had annoyed the Pompadour so much that their chances of giving concerts at
Versailles were finished. Leopold was already looking
anxiously in his purse, thinking that they couldn't afford
to stay in Paris much longer, when a messenger arrived
with a letter bearing the Royal Seal!

'Mamma! Children! Listen to this!' he cried excitedly.
'We are invited *to stay at the Palace of Versailles*!'

'To *stay*!' Mamma gasped.

'Yes! "Until such time as it is His Majesty's pleasure
to command us to play for him!"'

'Did the King sign the letter himself?' asked Nannerl.

'No, no. It is from one of the Managers of the Court Pleasures – Monsieur Favart.'

At once Mamma began worrying all over again about whether they should all have new clothes made for the occasion, but Papa thought that they all had quite enough, and they probably wouldn't be invited to any Court Balls anyway. They were expected to arrive on December 24th.

This time one of the Palace coaches was sent to the Hotel Beauvais to fetch them, and they rode into Versailles feeling very grand indeed.

Their rooms – two of them, this time – were small enough, and very far from the Royal Apartments; but Mamma was glad they were no bigger, for there was never enough wood to keep a good fire in all day, and their man-servant, Sebastian, had a difficult time trying to beg more from other Palace servants.

'Brrr!' Leopold shivered. 'Don't these French nobles ever feel the cold? I'd rather be back on the third floor at home in Salzburg. I wonder what the Hagenauers and all our friends are doing now? Making merry, I expect, and having a good old German Christmas!'

This made Mamma very sad and homesick, so they all had to try and cheer her up. It was a strange Christmas for this little family, so very far from home, with not enough money to buy each other presents. But Sebastian rose to the occasion, helped Mamma with the cooking, and stole special titbits from the Royal Kitchen for them to eat.

'At least,' Mamma said philosophically, 'we are all together, as a family should be at Christmas time.'

'Christmas doesn't mean as much to the French as it does to us,' Papa said. 'They make much more fuss about New Year's Eve.'

Sure enough, on the morning of December 31st, a courtier brought them a message from the King. 'Their Majesties command you to play for them this afternoon, and you are invited to attend the Royal Dinner tomorrow.'

'The King invites us to dine with him?' Leopold's eyes popped out of his head.

The courtier frowned. 'No, monsieur. You will dine with the kitchen staff. You are invited *to be present* when their Majesties dine.'

'I see,' Leopold said. 'Well, I suppose that is quite an honour in itself.' He bowed solemnly. 'We are their Majesties' humble servants, and we are proud to accept their invitation.'

That afternoon they were all taken to a small private theatre in the Palace, and gave a long concert. Wolfgang and Marianne went through all their usual parlour tricks, and as a Grand Finale Wolfgang improvised on any tune the audience cared to give him.

But this wasn't the end of the concert, for King Louis xv had three daughters, Adelaide, Henriette and Victoire, who were all quite good musicians. Princess Adelaide played the violin, Princess Henriette played a kind of old-fashioned 'cello called the *viola da gamba,* and Princess Victoire was passably good at the clavier. The three girls insisted on coming on to the stage to play quartets and quintets with Wolfgang and Nannerl, and they were so pleased with themselves and with the children that they hugged and kissed them and gave them presents and sweets.

'You see?' Wolfgang said triumphantly to his father afterwards. 'The three Princesses were not too proud to kiss us, any more than our own Empress. Who does that Madame de Pompadour think she is, I'd like to know?'

Next day, New Year's Day, the Mozarts played minuets

and gavottes for the Court to dance to, and then came the banquet. To their delight, they were allowed to stand behind the King's and Queen's chairs while they ate.

'At least we're near the fire,' Leopold whispered to his wife. 'Those poor devils at the far end of the room must be freezing.' (Those poor devils were some of the greatest nobles in France.) 'Who'd live in a Palace for choice? Why, the food must be stone cold by the time it gets to the end of the table!'

The King didn't take much notice of the Mozarts. 'They say he's rather shy,' Mamma told Nannerl. But Queen Marie was kindness itself.

'I don't think she likes being a Queen very much,' Leopold said later. 'They say that our concert is the only Court entertainment she has enjoyed for months. She never goes to masked balls or anything like that. She just likes staying at home with her family.'

Queen Marie talked to Wolfgang a lot – and in German, too. The boy was thankful to be able to speak his own language for a change; it was a strain, talking French all day and trying not to lose his temper when people at Court made fun of his accent.

'Try a little of this,' the Queen would say, handing him a morsel of food on the end of a fork. 'Tell me how you like it.'

Wolfgang, who was getting terribly hungry because the Mozarts had to wait until the Court had finished eating before they got their own dinner in the kitchens, gobbled it up with interest.

'Not bad,' he said candidly. 'What is it?'

'*Your Majesty,*' Mamma reminded him in a whisper.

'What is it, Your Majesty?' Wolfgang asked.

'Why, have you never had quails in aspic before?' laughed the Queen.

'No, Madame,' the boy replied. 'We generally have liver dumplings and sauerkraut at home.'

'Liver dumplings?' exclaimed the King, in his odd, husky, high-pitched tones. 'What on earth are they?' There was a roar of laughter from the other diners.

'They are a great delicacy in Germany,' said the Queen politely. 'Also in Poland, where I come from.'

'They would be a little too heavy for our French taste,' smiled the King.

Leopold Mozart whispered to Mamma, 'The King, poor fellow, hardly touches a thing. They say he suffers terribly from indigestion.'

'So would we if we ate all that rich food,' Mamma replied disapprovingly. 'Just look at that sideboard!' She nodded towards a long table loaded with boars' heads, stuffed turkeys, game, fruit and sweetmeats of all kinds. 'It's all very well sneering at the simple food we have at home, but we're much healthier than they are!'

But when at last the Mozarts did get something to eat, finishing up the glorious dishes on the sideboard with the servants (who stole legs of turkey, and anything else they could wrap up in a handkerchief and smuggle home to their families), Mamma ate as heartily as anyone.

They stayed another week at Versailles, and played several times for the Princesses and their friends. One of them, the Countess of Tesse, asked Wolfgang to write some music specially for her; so he wrote four little sonatas for violin and clavier, and dedicated two to the Countess, and two to his special friend, Princess Victoire.

Just before they were due to return to Paris, Sebastian Winter came very nervously to Leopold and said, 'Sir, I wish to give in my notice.'

'Your notice? But, Sebastian, why? Don't I pay you enough? Aren't you happy with us?'

'It isn't that, sir. I have been very happy serving your family. But I can't stand this sort of life. The other servants keep mocking me because my clothes and manners are so foreign and unfashionable.' The poor fellow was almost in tears. 'I am a simple German, sir, and these extravagant ways are not for me. I will, of course, stay with you until you find another man to replace me.'

Leopold begged him to stay but it was no use. 'I cannot promise you that we will be returning to Salzburg next month, or any time this year,' he said. 'We are musicians and we have to go wherever we can find employment. Have you been offered another post?'

'Yes, sir. Prince Fürstenberg needs a barber and wig-curler at his Court. The master of his household thinks I would be suitable.'

'But where shall I find another manservant?' Leopold groaned. 'Good ones are very hard to come by.'

In the end it was Sebastian himself who found one. 'His name is Jean-Pierre Poitevin,' he announced. 'He has been in service at the British Embassy. He comes from Alsace, and is very honest.'

Very honest he may have been, but he was also very stupid.

'Really, he is the clumsiest fellow I ever saw,' said Leopold, in despair, after Sebastian had been gone a week and Jean-Pierre had taken over his job. 'He cannot tie a cravat without dropping it on the floor a dozen times, and he speaks such funny dialects of both French and German, that I can hardly understand a word he says!'

At any rate, the Mozarts were busy enough now. 'It is exactly as Grimm said it would be,' Leopold said. 'Once you have played at Court you get invited everywhere!'

One of the houses where they were often asked to play was Prince Conti's. Here they met all the famous people in Paris, and all the foreign ambassadors too. Wolfgang astonished them all by his improvisation. Like all really good musicians, he was at his very best when he was simply making it up as he went along.

'If only there were some kind of musical shorthand!' sighed Princess Galitzine. 'To think that nobody will ever be able to write down music as fast as this boy invents it!'

Princess Galitzine was the wife of Prince Galitzine, the Russian Ambassador. He was very friendly to the Mozarts, and so was the British Ambassador, who was the Duke of Bedford. They were both very interested in Wolfgang and Nannerl, and stood on each side of Leopold Mozart, trying to persuade him to bring his wonderful children to their own countries.

'Your Excellencies are most kind,' Leopold said, with his politest bows. 'We shall hope to accept your invitations if my wife's health will allow us to travel so far.'

There were several other musicians at Prince Conti's and two of them were German. Herr Eckhart, who came from Augsburg, where Leopold had been born, was friendliness itself, and full of praise for the two children. But Herr Schobert, who was afraid that Prince Conti would ask the Mozarts to stay in Paris permanently, was jealous and treated them very sourly.

There were other concerts at Monsieur Félix's house in the Rue Saint-Honoré, and here Wolfgang and Nannerl played in Monsieur Félix's private theatre. He was one of the richest men in Paris, and he loved to have operas performed and concerts arranged specially for his friends.

Whenever they had a moment to spare, Mamma and Papa Mozart talked about the future. What Papa had said about Mamma's health was not the only consideration.

'Russia is very far off,' he said. 'Moscow and St Petersburg are fifteen hundred miles away, and it would take us at least a month of riding in terrible coaches over fearfully rough country to get there. And if we had to spend the winter there, heaven help us! I have heard that the winter is so cold there that a man's nose can fall off with frostbite!'

'Why not go to England first?' Mamma suggested. 'It is nearer, although people say that the Channel crossing is one of the most dreadful voyages in the world.'

'I can't pretend to look forward to a sea journey,' sighed Leopold, who had never been in a boat in his life. 'But I hear that they treat foreign artists generously there, and spend plenty of golden guineas on entertainment, and we could certainly do with some guineas, though we haven't done at all badly with *louis d'or* in Paris! The English are business-like; they pay in cash, which we badly need. As it is, we have enough gold snuffboxes and suchlike to open a curio shop!'

'Gold is not so bad,' said Mamma wisely. 'It doesn't lose value when you travel from country to country. But when you change your money at frontiers, you lose some of it if you aren't very careful.'

'At any rate,' Leopold said, 'London isn't so far away— only three hundred miles as the crow flies.'

'But, Papa,' interrupted Wolfgang seriously, 'we are not crows!'

The family roared with laughter at this, which pleased little Wolfgang because he thought he had said something very witty indeed.

'I think the Duke of Bedford is a sincere man,' said Papa. 'He will help us all he can, and mention our names to the Court at St James's Palace. Besides, in London musicians are allowed to give concerts, and sell the tickets themselves, just as they please. That would be a nice change from having to wait for kings and queens and lords and ladies to give their permission, and invite us, and make us feed with the servants, and all that sort of nonsense we have been used to. Yes, I think we will try England in the spring. What do you think of that, children? Would you like to cross the sea?'

'Oh, *yes*, Papa!' they cried; and Wolfgang at once wanted to know how big the sea was, and was it bigger than the Danube, which they had seen at Linz, and was it even wider than the Wolfgang Lake in Austria (which was the largest piece of water any of them had ever seen), and how many days would it take to get there, and would they be starting tomorrow, and a hundred other questions.

And soon Wolfgang forgot about Paris, and the Palace of Versailles, and all the wonderful things they had seen there, and sang over and over again, 'We're going to see the sea! We're going to see the sea!'

6

Over the Channel

If you had asked Wolfgang Mozart what he expected the sea to be like, he would probably have said, 'Oh, it will be deep blue, with little ripples on the top, and mountains in the distance, and a deep blue sky above it with one or two little white clouds, and little villages all along the edge of the water.' For that was how he remembered the Austrian lakes.

Nannerl could not stop staring at the sea. She had never seen waves breaking before, and Leopold tried to explain to her about the tides.

'But why, Papa?' she kept asking. 'Why does the sea run away and come back again?'

'My dear, they say it has something to do with the moon, but you must ask some learned scientist, for I can't tell you!'

It wasn't so bad the night they arrived at Calais; at least you could see the white cliffs of Dover on the horizon. But the next morning, when they woke up in their damp, musty inn, it was almost as dark as night, with a buffeting wind and drenching rain. The only ships they could see were all clustered together in the harbour, their sails furled and their masts heaving and rolling in the gale, and their timbers groaning as if they would split at any moment.

After breakfast Leopold went down to the harbour to see if he could get a passage to Dover for the four of them. He came back to the inn full of gloom.

'Not a ship will venture out until the wind drops,' he said. 'The sailors say they have no idea when they will put out, or whether they'll have berths for us when they do. The packet from England is late, and even if it arrives tomorrow, it won't be going back for at least a week.'

'We must get another servant, Leopold,' Mamma reminded him. 'At least while we're waiting we can be looking for a man. He must be able to speak English too, for we certainly can't.'

The Mozarts, who were at home anywhere where German, French and Italian were spoken, hadn't a word of English between them. 'And London is just as full of rogues as Paris, I've heard,' Leopold warned. 'We're sure to be swindled if we don't have someone to translate for us.'

'Jean-Pierre wouldn't have been any use, even if he'd stayed with us,' Mamma said. 'He'd have dropped our luggage in the sea, and muddled our money, and, anyway, he didn't speak French properly, let alone English.'

'Poor fellow,' Leopold laughed. 'When he heard we were going to England, he turned quite green. Said he wouldn't sail on the sea if we paid him a thousand *louis*!'

'I've been talking to the innkeeper,' Mamma said. 'He says that if we haven't got a servant of our own, the only thing to do is to find one of those men who are always hanging about the harbour, hoping to earn a tip by carrying people's bags. At least we'll be able to find a man to come with us as far as Dover, and after that we'll have to find an English one.'

'Hm.' Leopold frowned. 'They looked a pretty evil lot, those fellows I saw on the quayside this morning. But I expect you're right, my dear.'

And that is how Porta came into their lives. He had only one eye. His clothes were ragged, and his hat so dirty that they wondered if he ever took it off even when he went to bed. He said he had been a soldier and a sailor and a handyman and a cook, and he had scars on his face and a broken nose as if he had been in a hundred fights. And yet there was a sort of cheerful impudence about him, as if he never allowed life to get him down, that made them laugh and like him.

'Though whether we can trust him, I really don't know,' Leopold shrugged.

Two days passed, and still the gale blew and the rain came driving down. On the third day, Porta came running to the inn in great excitement. 'Master! Master!' he cried, 'I have found an English skipper who is willing to take you. He says not to wait for the mail boat, but that you should hire his fishing boat for your family. When it's too rough to fish, he takes passengers!'

Leopold shuddered. 'What is his price?'

'Five *louis,* sir.'

'Five *louis* for a journey of little more than twenty miles? The man is mad.'

'Five *louis* for the sailboat alone, sir. There is an extra charge for the rowing boat.'

'What rowing boat?'

'Why, sir, the boat which takes you from the shore to the sailboat! And there is another rowing boat which takes you off the sailboat and into Dover Harbour when it's low tide.'

'Why on earth don't they land us at high tide then?'

Porta winked his one eye. 'Why, sir, because they wouldn't get so much money!'

'It's scandalous!' Leopold Mozart clenched his fists. 'And you, you rogue, what profit do *you* make on this?'

'Oh, none that you'd notice, sir,' the fellow replied meekly. 'Besides, I have arranged things for you so that you will save at least two *louis d'or*!'

'How's that?'

'Why, sir, you are to share the boat with another family of four, at a cost of only three *louis*!'

'That's better. It is still very expensive, though.'

'Not for the time it will take at this season of the year, sir. April is a bad month for the Channel, sir. A pity you couldn't have chosen almost any other month, sir!'

'Oh dear!' Mamma moaned. 'I feel ill already!'

Poor Mamma. She suffered more than any of them. She laid in supplies of food for them to eat on board, but for two days they were all so ill that they could hardly swallow so much as a crust of bread. They lay on the floor of a rough cabin trying to sleep, while the ship pitched up and down as if they were alternately falling down a well and being carried up to the clouds by an eagle. The mess and the misery and the foulness of it all were beyond description. Whenever the wind dropped for a little while, they struggled up on deck and tried to get some benefit from the fresh air, but soon their legs buckled beneath them, and they tottered to the side to be sick again, and then down to the cabin to try to get some sleep.

On the third morning it was calm. They went up on deck and were most excited to see cliffs only a few miles away. 'England at last!' Leopold said fervently.

'It looks almost the same as France,' Wolfgang said, puzzled.

A roar of laughter from the sailors greeted this remark. 'Well said, youngster! You're right! We had to turn about yester evening, the wind was so strong! Never mind, sir, we'll have another try to get across today!'

Leopold was almost in despair. 'At least I'm getting used to it a bit,' he said. 'In fact, I think I could even eat some dinner!'

'I hope you can, sir!' laughed the sailors. 'We'll have good fishing today, and we'll warrant you never tasted a Dover sole before. It's the finest fish in the world.'

That evening the gale blew up again, but now it seemed to have veered round to the south and, by next morning, when they went on deck, it was the cliffs of Dover they saw, not Cape Gris Nez. By now they had all got their sea legs, although Mamma was still feeling rather shaky, and Wolfgang and Nannerl had a wonderful time clambering about the ship and getting in the sailors' way.

At night the sailors sang strange songs, some gentle and melancholy, some gay and roaring. 'They are called sea shanties, sir,' Porta explained. Wolfgang's head was ring-

ing with them by the end of the voyage, and he wished
that his music paper was not buried at the bottom of his
trunk, because he longed to write down the exciting frag-
ments of themes they suggested to his mind. Now that he
felt well again, the very wildness of the sea and its storms
seemed to make an even mightier music in his mind,
music that needed a whole orchestra to play, a whole choir
to sing.

'But first you must learn orchestration, Wolfgang,' his
father said. 'And before you learn that, you must learn to
write a quartet, to harmonise in four parts, whether for
instruments or voices. If we could all write down the music
we hear in our minds, what great composers we should
be! There is so much to learn, so many rules to master
before you can be allowed to break them, as great composers always do when they discover new sounds and new
forms!'

It was a comparatively cheerful Mozart family, though
dirty and bedraggled, that jumped, with all their great
load of baggage, into a rowing boat at Dover and were
pulled ashore.

And now they were completely in Porta's hands. He
arranged everything, tipped the porters, booked their seats
on the stage coach to London, found an inn for them to
stay the night, and paid their bill when they left in the
morning.

The London coach was the finest Wolfgang had ever
seen. He was particularly impressed by the red-coated
guard who rode behind with a loaded blunderbuss to pro-
tect them against highwaymen. When at last they were
settled inside, Porta said he was sorry, but he would have
to leave them now. He had taught them how to ask for
things in English, how to say 'good' and 'bad' and 'good
morning', and 'how much', and given them a rough idea

of those terribly confusing coins, guineas and shillings and crowns and pence and farthings. Leopold had written it all down in his notebook so that he shouldn't forget it.

'Well, I'm sorry to lose him,' said Leopold when they were jolting along the Dover Road. 'I'm sure he added ten or fifteen per cent to all our bills, as well as his wages, but we'd have been worse off without him. An entertaining rascal. I expect he'll go back to Calais and find some other simpletons like ourselves. No doubt that's how he makes his living. I wonder if we'll ever see him again?'

In fact, they *did* meet Porta again, six years later, but that is part of another chapter.

They stopped for dinner at the Royal Star Inn, Maidstone, where they tasted English roast beef for the first time, and very good it was, too.

'It makes a nice change from that eternal fricassée of chicken we used to have in France,' Mamma said. She smiled to Papa. 'It's good to see the children eating heartily again! I thought we should never be able to touch another bit of food after that dreadful sea voyage!'

Towards nightfall the wheels of the coach thundered on to the cobbled streets of London.

'So this is the famous Piccadilly!' said Papa, looking out of the window. It was misty as well as dark, and the only light came from the flaming torches carried by the link boys, who crowded round the coach shouting that they would light passengers to their lodgings for a penny.

But this the Mozarts did not need, for they were able to get a room for a few nights at the inn itself, which was called the White Bear. The innkeeper spoke a little French, and Papa gave him a message from Porta who, it seemed, had an arrangement with the White Bear by which all the passengers he conducted across the Channel had first choice of rooms there.

'It's far too expensive for us to stay here long,' Papa said. 'I will start looking around for some cheap lodgings. Be careful, all of you, while I am gone. There are more rogues and highwaymen around London than in any other city of Europe, I have been told. Carry no money about with you, and go everywhere by sedan chair. It's worth the fearful cost to be safe from attack. The landlord tells me there were two cases last week of defenceless women being held up at pistol point by a rascal in Hyde Park, which is only a few hundred yards from here!'

Later that day, Papa came back to the White Bear and announced that he had found lodgings near St Martin's Lane, in Cecil Court.

'Our host is a barber, Mr Cousins. Now there's a bit of luck! He can curl our wigs and shave me every day at a reduced price. Moreover, his customers are among the most fashionable people in London. He says he can introduce us to Dr Burney and Mr Goldsmith and Mr Garrick, and many other people connected with the theatre.'

Mamma was doubtful about this. 'They say English people go to the theatre far too often, and that the plays are frivolous and vulgar,' she said. 'I hope it will not be necessary for our children to go into theatres.'

As soon as they were settled in their new home, Papa went to the Austrian Embassy to see whether there was any chance of giving a concert at Court. He came back full of excitement.

'Most of the fashionable folk are out of London,' he said. 'So we shan't sell many tickets if we hire a hall to give a concert. But in June – in two months' time – everybody will be coming back to Town for the King's Birthday celebrations on June 4th. Then this sinful city will be at its gayest, and the lords and ladies will be throwing their money about on any diversion of the moment.'

'But, Papa, tell us about St James's Palace!' cried Nannerl.

'Well, it is all arranged! Apparently the King and Queen have heard about the Mozarts already! We are famous, my dears!'

'But *when,* Papa? *When?'* Wolfgang jumped up and down impatiently.

'Why, *tomorrow!'* Leopold laughed.

'Tomorrow!' Mamma was dismayed. 'But we have been in London only four days! And I shall have to get your Court clothes cleaned and ironed, and, oh, Leopold, the children will have no time to practise, and it is nearly three weeks since either of them touched a clavier or a violin!'

'We can't help that,' Papa said cheerfully. 'Mr Cousins has an old spinet in his parlour which is terribly out of tune, but it is good enough for a few keyboard exercises just to keep us in trim. Look, here is our invitation!'

He showed them a stiff piece of paper with 'St James's Palace' written at the top. 'Notice that it says that Herr Mozart and his family are *invited* to play before Their Majesties, not *commanded.* They treat musicians like gentlefolk in England!'

As usual, Wolfgang was full of questions. What were the King and Queen of England like? Were they very old? Would the Queen kiss them as the Empress of Austria had done, or would she be haughty and stuck-up like Madame de Pompadour?

'All I know of King George and Queen Charlotte is that they are Germans, and can talk to us in our own language,' Papa replied. 'Thank goodness for that. I can't get on with this mincing English language!'

'Germans? But, Papa, how can a German be King of England?'

'Well, he is King of Hanover too, that's why; and so was his father, and so was his grandfather before that.'

'Then why isn't the King of France an Englishman?' Wolfgang demanded. 'And why isn't our Empress a Frenchwoman?'

'That's enough questions!' cried Papa in despair. 'Come, we must get ready for the concert.'

At St James's Palace everyone treated them very kindly. Wolfgang soon found out that there wasn't nearly so much bowing and curtseying.

The Mozarts felt at home immediately in this Palace, which wasn't nearly as big and draughty as either Schönbrunn or Versailles.

'But I hear the King finds it too small, and has just bought Buckingham House, which he is extending. Had we arrived next year instead of this, I suppose we should have been summoned to that great building,' said Papa Mozart. He sighed. 'A pity that Kings and Queens must always live in such huge, cold places!'

The King was a plump, youngish man of 26. His Queen was not as beautiful as the Empress of Austria, Wolfgang noticed, but she smiled a lot and seemed very kind. Leopold whispered in German for a few minutes with a stocky young man who had a square sort of face and big black eyebrows, and then the concert began.

First Nannerl played, and then Wolfgang. He played the same piece by Wagenseil that he had played for the composer himself in Vienna. The Royal audience clapped as if they had enjoyed it, but not quite so enthusiastically as the King of France's daughters had applauded.

Suddenly the King got up from his chair and came over to the clavier. Wolfgang slipped off his stool and bowed, but the King made him sit down again. Wolfgang couldn't understand why the King had come to him instead of making him walk over to his chair.

'Not bad, my boy. Not bad at all, hey, what?' said the King in his squeaky, husky voice. 'Can you read music at sight?'

'Oh yes, sir.'

'Well, try this.' King George rummaged in a pile of music, chose a piece and set it on the music stand. 'Too difficult for you, hey?'

'No, sir. At least, I don't think so.'

In fact, it was the beginning of an oratorio for choir and organ by Handel, but the King, who couldn't read music, didn't know that it wasn't arranged for the clavier. It made no difference to Wolfgang. He rearranged the parts at sight, and played several pages. This time the Court was rapturous, and the King roared with delight.

'Handel, that's the stuff!' he said gruffly. 'Don't really like any other music. Purcell's not bad, and Dr Arne's pretty good. But Handel—never been anyone else like him. Died five years ago, poor fellow. Know any more Handel, boy?'

Wolfgang and Nannerl knew plenty, and played Handel until Queen Charlotte said, 'The children must be tired, my dear. Let them have a rest, I beg you!'

'Nonsense, Charlotte. They're young and full of energy. How about giving us a song, my dear? The boy will accompany you.'

And so Wolfgang found himself playing Henry Purcell's 'Fairest Isle', while the Queen of England sang in her pleasant, weak little voice.

Meanwhile the black-browed young man had been watching Wolfgang with growing astonishment. He now came over to the clavier and asked Leopold, 'Can the boy improvise on a ground bass?'

'Certainly, Herr Bach.'

Herr Bach smiled. 'Try this, my boy.' He put some scribbled notes before Wolfgang. 'That is the bass part of a dance by Handel. I want you to make up a tune on top of it, and mind you get the right harmonies in between!'

'Y-yes, Herr Bach!' For the first time Wolfgang was nervous. 'You are *really* Herr Bach?' he asked.

'I am my father's son,' the young man smiled.

'You are the son of the great Johann Sebastian Bach?' the boy murmured, as if he were in a dream.

'Johann *Christian* Bach, at your service,' the young man laughed. 'I'm afraid my father and I disagreed a good deal about music, though. I like the Italian style, and he was always faithful to the old German music. I have the honour to be' – he bowed towards the King and Queen – 'Her Majesty's music teacher.'

'Herr Bach has most generously promised to give *you* some lessons, too, Wolfgang,' said Leopold.

'Come,' the King interrupted. 'Let us hear what the boy can do!'

Wolfgang soon overcame his nervousness, and upon those simple bass notes there grew a lovely melody with the most ingenious decorations, as his small fingers picked their way about the keyboard. When it ended, the Court was in an uproar of applause. Herr Bach just stared at the tiny figure at the clavier and murmured, 'Unbelievable! Unbelievable! How old did you say your son was, Herr Mozart? Only *eight*? Unbelievable!'

When at last it was time to go, the King thanked the Mozarts for their music, and said, 'We shall hope to see more of your clever children while you are in London, Mr Mozart! Good day to you.' And as they were leaving the Palace, one of the Gentlemen-in-Waiting handed Leopold a purse containing twenty-four golden guineas.

7

Summer in London

The next few days were fine and sunny, and the Mozarts
decided to do a little sight-seeing. Really, London was
completely different from any other city they had ever
visited. 'There are so many parks, so much country in the
middle of the City!' Mamma said wonderingly.

Nannerl was so interested in everything that she began
to keep a diary. In it she wrote down all the places they
visited. They went to the Tower of London, where there

were lions in cages whose roaring was really quite frightening, so that Wolfgang turned pale and held his father's arm very tightly. They saw the remains of Old London Bridge, which was like a higgledy-piggledy street of houses crossing the River Thames, built upon arches so close together that the water seemed to be always on the point of washing them away. It was being pulled down now, and the foundations of a wide, modern bridge had been laid beside it. You could still pick your way across the rubble of the old bridge, however. Indeed, it was almost the only way of getting to Southwark, where they went to church on Sundays. Sometimes they crossed the river by boat, which Wolfgang much preferred, though Papa thought it was far too expensive.

They visited St Paul's Cathedral too, which fascinated Papa, because it was so like St Peter's in Rome; and the strange Monument to the Great Fire of London, which Mamma thought very ugly. Somerset House pleased them all, and so did Lincoln's Inn Fields – another bit of country in the middle of the City – and Temple Bar, a huge arch standing between the Strand and cobbled, smelly old Fleet Street.

'These English are a strange people,' Papa said. They were standing in the Strand watching boys playing football up and down the street, all among the horses and carts and sedan chairs. 'Fancy allowing a savage game like this to be played in one of the main streets in London, to the danger of the public!'

Indeed, there were a lot of things about England that puzzled poor Papa Mozart. 'Their manners are so careless!' he said. 'Why, in the House of Commons, where they meet to govern the country, I'm told they crack nuts, and loll with their coats unbuttoned and their feet on the bench in front of them! And in a tavern you cannot tell whether a man is a gentleman or not, except by the way he speaks! And look how they dress! They leave their cravats untied, and their wigs unpowdered.'

'Surely, my dear, that is because wigs are going out of fashion in England!' Mamma put in. 'I was reading in a newspaper that the peruke-makers marched like soldiers to St James's Palace to protest to the King about it!'

'And people are so irreligious!' Papa went on. 'Why, when we looked into St Bride's Church the other day, there was Mr Dibdin, the organist, playing "Lilliburlero", a popular song, on the organ as a voluntary!'

For Wolfgang, the funniest thing in all London was to see people, on rainy days, walking about with a sort of round portable roof over their heads.

'But what *is* it, Papa?' he would ask, choking with laughter.

'It's called an umbrella,' Leopold answered solemnly. 'And you mustn't laugh, because it's very rude.'

They went for long walks in Hyde Park, as far as Tyburn; and here one day they saw something that wasn't easy to forget. It was Hanging Day, which happened about once a fortnight, and highwaymen and wretched thieves who had stolen a few pence or a bite to eat were executed in public.

Best of all, they liked St James's Park. Here the young beaux of London went to look at the pretty girls (and, no doubt, the pretty girls went to look at them too), and people played games like chuck-farthing and skittles. Skittles was Wolfgang's favourite game, and very good at it he was.

It was in St James's Park one morning that the Royal Carriage came along on its way from Buckingham House to the City. The Mozarts politely doffed their hats and bowed, and to their astonishment the carriage stopped.

They saw a gentleman waving his hat and a gold-topped cane to them from the window, and heard a hearty voice shouting: 'Good day to you, Mr Mozart! And how is your family? Well, I trust?'

'Indeed, very well, I thank Your Majesty!' Papa gasped. The King had recognised them!

'A fine morning, is it not? And how is the young man, eh?'

'I'm very well, thank you, sir!' stammered Wolfgang.

'A second Handel, sir! That's what you are! When are you coming to play for us again, hey, my boy?'

'Whenever Your Majesty pleases!' Wolfgang said.

'Excellent! We'll send you a letter, young fellow, hey, what?'

The King's head popped back inside the window, and the Royal Carriage went on its way, leaving the Mozarts staring after it.

'Well, did you ever hear of such a thing!' Papa's face was pink with pleasure. 'He actually recognised us, although we were in our ordinary clothes! Even our own Empress would never have spoken to us out of doors! I think there's something to be said for these free and easy manners after all. Now, do you know, that gives me an idea.'

Papa's idea was that Wolfgang should write a set of sonatas and dedicate it to the Queen. He had dedicated music to Princess Victoria in Paris, but never to a Queen before. But Queen Charlotte had been so friendly that Papa didn't think she would mind. So Wolfgang set to work, in odd moments when he had nothing in particular to do, curled up in a corner with the rest of the family chattering away all round him, and hardly bothering to try any of his ideas out on the clavier to hear how they sounded, he soon had them finished.

'H'm. Not bad, Wolferl,' Papa said when he saw them. They had been written so fast that it wasn't too easy to read the tumbling notes. 'Not bad, though you've used one or two very old ideas here and there, and your harmony's a bit shaky. What am I always telling you? You *can't* write consecutive fifths, they sound like a Chinese band.'

Wolfgang shouted with laughter. 'And when did you ever hear a Chinese band, Papa?'

'Never. But I have heard a Turkish band in Hungary, and it was much the same thing. Well, we'll make a few corrections and then get Herr Bach to look these sonatas over, and we'll see if he thinks they're good enough to present to the Queen.'

Papa was working very hard himself nowadays, organising a concert which he and the children were to give on June 5th. 'The King's birthday is on the fourth, so London will be full, and we should be able to sell quite a lot of tickets,' Papa said. 'I have followed Bach's advice and hired the Great Room in Spring Gardens. It'll cost us about five pounds, I'm afraid,' he sighed. 'And the lighting and music stands are extra, and we have to pay the other musicians too.'

'What other musicians, Papa?' Nannerl asked.

'Enough for a concerto or two,' Papa replied. 'In London, you see, we don't have to wait for lords and ladies to invite us to their houses, or for Archbishops to tell us what to do. In London, concerts have to be big and brilliant, or the public won't come. But people buy tickets, and don't just give us gold snuffboxes and things. Music is "business" –' he smiled as he used the strange English word – 'and for my part I'm not sorry! Let me see, now, six guineas for the principal singers, half a guinea each for the orchestra and three guineas for their leader, half a guinea for each clavier . . .' he scribbled some figures on a piece of paper and frowned over them.

'Are we playing on two claviers then, Papa?' Wolfgang asked.

'Yes, the same duets that you played for the Princesses at Versailles.'

Next morning Mamma came running to Papa, waving a newspaper called the *Public Advertiser*. 'They've written an article about Wolferl! It says the funniest things, and some of them aren't true at all. Look!'

Papa looked rather awkward. 'Er – well, it isn't exactly an *article,* my dear – it's an advertisement. I – er – wrote most of it myself, as a matter of fact.'

'Listen to this!' Mamma cried wonderingly. 'It says Wolfgang and Nannerl are "prodigies of nature", and that Wolfgang is "another Handel", just as King George said; and – oh, heavens! that a boy should hear such extravagant praise of himself! – "The celebrated and astonishing Master MOZART, lately arrived, a child of seven years of age –"'

'That's not true!' Wolfgang said crossly. 'I'm eight and a half!'

'Don't interrupt, dear! " – will perform five select Pieces of his own Composition, which have already given the highest Pleasure, Delight and Surprise to the greatest Judges of Music in England, and Italy."'

'But I've never been to Italy!' gasped Wolfgang.

'I'm afraid Mr Phillips insisted on putting that bit in,' Papa mumbled. 'He's the manager of advertisements at the newspaper. He said it sounded better, because the Italians are considered to know everything about music.'

' – "and Master Mozart is justly esteemed the most extraordinary Prodigy and most amazing Genius that has appeared in any age,"' Mamma finished breathlessly.

Wolfgang solemnly squatted on the floor, put his head down, and rolled neatly over. 'There,' he said calmly. 'Tell people I can turn somersaults as well. And whistle between my teeth. And waggle my ears. And beat my old Papa at billiards!' he laughed, affectionately tweaking his father's nose.

'Come along, Amazing Genius, and get your breakfast,' said Mamma. 'You won't have any energy for practising.'

Tuesday, June 5th, was a day of brilliant sunshine, cooling to an evening of gentle radiance. Leopold Mozart, hovering anxiously at the doors of the Great Room in Spring Gardens, watched the smart people in their evening clothes arriving in coaches and phaetons and sedan chairs, some from Pall Mall with its splendid new pavements, some from Whitehall, some from the muddy Strand.

'You'd expect everybody to be going to the King's Theatre over there in Haymarket,' he whispered to Mamma, 'for they're giving a new opera by Dr Arne there. Or else you'd think people might be off to Chelsea for a stroll in the country and a glass of milk at the farm there. But no! All London is coming here, to our concert!'

It certainly seemed so. Papa Mozart was delighted to see Dr Burney and Dr Boyce, two of the leading composers in England, among the audience – he was introduced to them by Herr Carl Abel, the German *viola de gamba* player who lived in London and was a friend of Herr Bach.

The candles in the great chandeliers were lighted, and through the tall windows the orange sunset peered, as the music began. First there was a Bach concerto, played by the best musicians in London. Then Wolfgang and Nannerl played their clavier duet, and the audience applauded wildly.

'The English don't only clap their hands,' Papa whispered to the children in great surprise. 'They stamp their feet, and bang their walking sticks on the floor, too! This would be very bad manners in Austria, but here people don't mind showing their enthusiasm!'

Now came Wolfgang's big performance – his own sonatas, with Papa playing the violin; and in the middle they changed over, with Wolfgang playing the violin. At this the audience got to its feet and roared with delight, and people in the front rows came right into the orchestra and lifted the boy shoulder-high.

Papa, flushed with excitement, tried to calm everyone down, and shouted, 'Please, ladies and gentlemen, we still have several more pieces to play, if you will allow us!'

After a short interval, Papa conducted the orchestra in a Haydn symphony, and then Nannerl and Wolfgang played some Italian pieces, followed by Wolfgang alone – on the organ this time – playing some extremely difficult fugues of Bach. In the grand finale, Wolfgang and Nannerl played with the whole orchestra, conducted by Papa Mozart.

The audience cheered, and Dr Boyce and Dr Burney came among the instrumentalists and shook their hands warmly; and Lord Thanet and other leaders of musical society made them promise to visit their houses and give private concerts as well. The children were very tired – they had been playing, on and off, for three hours! – and in the little office behind the Great Room they sank into chairs as if they wanted to fall asleep there and then.

'Children, what do you think!' Papa cried triumphantly. 'We have taken over a hundred pounds tonight! Didn't I say there were golden guineas to be earned in London? Now we must pay the musicians. Come with me, children.'

He hurried them back to the Great Room, where the

orchestra were packing up their instruments. 'Always be careful to thank the musicians who have been playing with you,' he whispered, as they entered. 'Gentlemen, please accept my humblest gratitude for your magnificent performance tonight. It has been a great honour for us to play with you. My children would like to thank you personally.'

Nannerl curtsied and said, 'T'ank you so mooch!' in her best English. Wolfgang bowed so deeply as he said his piece that he fell over and burst out laughing.

'And now, gentlemen,' Papa said, 'if you will step into the office at the back, my children and I will be delighted to pay you the fees we owe you.'

And here he had the surprise of his life. For the leader of the orchestra, Mr Beresford, stood with his arms round the two children and said quietly: 'No, Mr Mozart. We will not accept any fees at all. It has been a privilege to play with young musicians of such quality. You have already paid us for rehearsals, and we are all agreed that this will be enough.'

'But, Mr Beresford, I cannot allow –'

'Our minds are made up, sir!' smiled Mr Beresford. 'Please take the money you would have given us and put it by for your children's welfare. We look forward to playing with them again some time.'

There were tears in Papa Mozart's eyes, and his voice shook a little as he replied, 'You are good fellows. Long live the country where such warm hearts are to be found! And long live music, that inspires such comradeship among its artists!'

8

Chelsea and Concerts

The children slept late next morning, for they hadn't got to bed until eleven after the concert. Papa was so pleased with their success and the weather was so warm and sunny that he decided to give the whole family a special treat, so they hired a boat at Temple Stairs and rowed down the River Thames to Greenwich and back, taking a picnic lunch with them. Wolfgang had never seen so many ships in his life, their masts packed close together like trees in a forest.

On the way back, Mamma felt a little sad because the great wide river reminded her of the Danube and home; but Papa cheered her up by saying, 'Well, my dear, if we can earn enough money in London, there's no reason why we shouldn't think about going home in a few months' time. And perhaps we'll even have enough to buy a little house of our own in Salzburg! Wouldn't that be wonderful? Oh, I nearly forgot to tell you!'

He pulled an envelope out of his pocket. 'This letter came from Herr Hagenauer this morning! And he sends us a piece out of the *Salzburg News,* all about Wolfgang and Nannerl and how they were received by the King and Queen at St James's Palace! So they haven't forgotten about us at home, you see!'

When they got back to their lodgings in Cecil Court that evening, Mrs Cousins, the landlord's wife, had a celebration dinner ready for them — calf's heart pudding, with cabbage, a special delicacy of hers — and very good it was too.

But the following morning they were all back at work again, rehearsing for a big charity concert at Ranelagh Gardens in three weeks' time.

'This time,' Papa said, 'we will not accept any money, for the concert is in aid of a new hospital. We can well afford it, for we have enough concerts to see us through the next few months.'

Ranelagh Gardens was a pretty little park near the village of Chelsea, a couple of miles outside London. Behind it was the Royal Hospital, where the old soldiers in their red coats could be seen taking their daily walks, hobbling on crutches or leaning on sticks, smoking their long clay pipes and fighting their battles over again. In front of it was the river, fringed with trees and here and there a farmhouse or a shepherd's cottage.

D

The concert was to be given in the Chinese Temple in the Gardens – a half-open, strange-looking building which was big enough for the musicians and a few of the audience.

'God willing, the weather will be fine,' said Papa anxiously. 'For if it rains, I don't know what will happen to most of the audience, who will have to sit in the open air.'

God willing, it *didn't* rain. And because most of the listeners sat out of doors, the orchestra was strengthened with horns and clarinets – more than the Mozarts had ever seen before.

'Wind instruments carry farther than strings in the open air,' Papa said. 'And the English, I have heard, play them particularly well.'

Looking back on that concert many years afterwards, Wolfgang thought it one of the happiest times of his young life. It was a picture of England that he never forgot. The fashionable men and women in their finest clothes, their carriages and horses waiting in a line outside the Gardens, the warm fresh country air, the scent of flowers. How fond of gardens and flowers the English were! Above all, it was some of the best music he had ever taken part in.

When it was over, and the audience were strolling under the trees, taking a cup of tea or a glass of wine, little Wolfgang asked the clarinettists and horn-players dozens of questions. How big was their range? What were the difficulties? How did one arrange one's mouth to blow them? The musicians roared with laughter to see the small boy puffing out his cheeks, trying desperately to blow a clear note on a French horn.

'Papa,' he said, 'I simply must compose something for horns and clarinets. I think they're wonderful instruments!'

Suddenly he was aware of two men staring at him. One of them was an ordinary enough young man; the other, much older, so extraordinary-looking that Wolfgang for a moment was frightened. He was so huge and ungainly, and his eyes so heavy and staring, his wig so grubby-looking, his suit so crumpled, his legs so fat and his stockings so untidy, his breath so short — and yet he seemed to be well-known and much respected, for everyone bowed to him and said: 'Good day to you, Doctor.'

'So this is the boy, Bozzy!' said this strange gentleman. 'Quite a *wonder*-child, I hear!' (He had a strange way of speaking, and pronounced the word *'woonder'*. Wolfgang afterwards heard that people spoke like this in the Midlands and North of England.)

'Ay, sir,' said his companion, who also had an unusual accent, with rolling r's that reminded Wolfgang of the way people spoke German at home in Salzburg. 'The advertisement didna deceive us after all. The boy is indeed a genius.'

'Genius, sir! Genius!' laughed the huge man. 'When a dog walks upon its hind legs at a fair, we applaud, but we do not call it genius! The boy is skilful enough, and plays his instruments just as another boy will do sums in his head. But we shall not know if he is a genius until he grows up. Anyway, my dear Bozzy, what should a Scotchman know of music? The vile bagpipe is *your* music, I'll warrant!'

Wolfgang thought this sounded rather rude, and half expected the other gentleman to be angry. But it was clear that they were old friends, accustomed to chaffing each other, for the younger man burst out laughing and said: 'When you can play me a tune on the flageolet, sir, I will allow you to insult ma national music!'

The huge man roared with merriment. 'Who am I to

talk of music, for I can scarcely recognise "Lilliburlero" when I hear it! However, this young man played a great number of notes very fast, and Dr Burney says he made no mistake, so I should like to pay him my respects!'

'Allow us to introduce ourselves.' The young man bowed to Papa Mozart. 'This is Doctor Samuel Johnson, and I am James Boswell, at your service, sir!'

Papa said: 'I am deeply honoured, gentlemen. This is my daughter Marianne, and my son Wolfgang.' In a whisper he told the children: 'Doctor Johnson is a very famous and learned man. He wrote a Dictionary of the English Language, and it took him five years.'

'Your servant, sir,' murmured Nannerl and Wolfgang, with suitable curtsies and bows. Dr Johnson asked Papa questions about where the children had travelled, and at what great houses they had played, and whether it did not spoil the children's schooling to make them earn their living so young.

'I think not, sir,' said Papa Mozart. 'They attend a local school wherever we are, and I give them lessons myself. You will find, if you care to test them, that they have some Latin, and the boy especially is quick at arithmetic, and they speak some words of French and Italian as well as English.'

'You have taught them well, sir, that is plain.' The Doctor nodded emphatically. Then he fumbled in his pocket and produced two half-guineas. 'Study diligently, children, and continue to give pleasure to everyone who hears you. I wish you all good day, and fortunate travels.'

During the next few weeks the Mozarts gave several concerts, and earned plenty more guineas. One of them was at Lord Thanet's house in Grosvenor Square. To get there from St Martin's Lane was too far for Nannerl and Wolfgang to walk, so they took sedan chairs, Papa following on foot and carrying all the music to save the fare. On the way back, there was a sudden downpour of summer rain, and poor Papa was drenched to the skin.

'I was not feeling too well when we started out,' he told Mamma. 'My throat was sore, and my legs ached and trembled.' He sneezed so loudly that the whole house shook. 'Oh dear! I fear I have at last got one of those "colds" for which this country is so famous.'

Mamma made him bathe his feet in hot water, and packed him off to bed. Next morning he had a high fever. 'This is no English cold, my dear,' she said seriously. 'If you are no better by this evening, I think we must call a doctor, or at least an apothecary.'

In the evening Papa's fever seemed worse, and after a restless night the doctor was sent for. He arrived with bottles full of leeches, to bleed the patient, and boxes full of pills. 'Try them, sir, try them all,' Papa Mozart insisted. 'No doubt it is God's will, but I cannot afford to be ill. As it is, I shall have to cancel our concerts for the next week or two.'

The doctor did all he could, but next day Papa was coughing very badly and there was a splitting pain in his lungs. Mamma was terribly worried.

'Now, children,' she said. 'I'm afraid we cannot have any practising for the next week or so. Papa must be kept absolutely quiet. Please speak only in whispers, and don't disturb him. You can use the time to catch up on your lessons, and you, Wolferl, will work at your harmony exercises.'

But Wolfgang had another idea. 'I'm going to try and write a symphony,' he announced. 'I've never written anything for full orchestra before, but I've been looking at some of Papa's scores and I think I know how to arrange it. I've got the first movement in my head already!'

'Well, so long as you have it all in your head, and don't try out any tunes on the clavier, and disturb poor Papa, I don't mind,' Mamma said. 'It will keep you out of mischief, anyway.'

So he sat in a corner with a quill pen and a bottle of ink and a pile of music paper, and stuck his tongue out of the corner of his mouth, and soon the pages were spattered with crotchets and quavers and breves and semibreves.

'I've given the horns plenty of good tunes to play,' he told Nannerl when she looked over his shoulder to see how he was getting on. 'For the London horn-players are the best I ever heard, and if only my symphony can be played while we are still in London, I shall be so excited!'

The weeks dragged on, and Papa recovered a little, though the fever had left him terribly weak. He was delighted to hear that Wolfgang was writing a long symphony for full orchestra, but Mamma would not let him see it yet. 'You'll only start correcting it, and you're not fit for work yet,' she said.

'Oh dear, what will become of us all if I don't get well by next week?' Papa worried. 'If we don't earn some more money soon, we shan't be able to afford the fare home to Salzburg.'

'Now, dear, you really must stop worrying,' Mamma said. 'We've always managed all right so far, and we shall go on managing. If you aren't well enough to organise concerts, I will learn to do it myself; or we will get Herr Bach to help us, or some of the many friends we have made in London.'

Two days later, the doctor called and said, 'Well, Mr Mozart, you're making good progress. Now you must take a holiday and get really fit. Frankly, I don't think this city air is good for you. I think you should move out nearer the country. What about Chelsea or Hampstead? Hampstead is on high ground, and very healthy; and it's a spa, too, with very beneficial mineral waters.'

Papa thought Hampstead was too far out unless they hired a carriage and horses. 'Chelsea is a charming village,' he said, 'and slightly less infested with highwaymen than Hampstead Heath. It will cost more, I daresay, but it will do us all good.'

'That gives me an idea,' said the doctor. 'I have a colleague, Dr Randal, who lives in Fivefields Row, between London and Chelsea. He has rooms to let, for the German students who have been lodging with him have just left and I expect he wants some new tenants.'

So it was arranged, and the Mozarts said goodbye to Mr Cousins the barber and moved to Fivefields Row, where the air was sweet and scented with the smell of nearby lavender fields, and the only sounds that broke the country silence were those of birds singing, goats bleating, and farm hands shouting to their horses.

Soon Papa was well enough to want to see the symphony Wolfgang had written. Great was his surprise when his eight-year-old son presented him with *two* symphonies!

'I got tired of waiting for you to get well so that you could see my first symphony, Papa,' he said. 'And we couldn't play any music because we were afraid of disturbing you. So I wrote another symphony, and here they both are!'

Papa Mozart was really astonished by what he saw. 'To be sure,' he told Mamma, 'there are mistakes in harmony, and he strives for effects which he can't possibly achieve until he knows more about composition, but the boy's not yet nine, after all!'

When Papa was well enough, he decided that they should all move back to London. 'With sedan chairs and carriages so expensive,' he said, 'it will be better to be near the city.' So they found lodgings in Thrift Street, in the village of Soho.

All London was preparing for the King's Anniversary – not his birthday, but the fourth anniversary of his coming to the throne. Once again the Mozarts were invited to St James's Palace, and this time Wolfgang presented his six little sonatas which he had written specially for Queen Charlotte, who gave him a present of fifty golden guineas.

'It's a long time since we had a family outing,' Papa announced one September morning. 'Let's all go and see an English opera! They are giving an old one at Drury Lane, by Mr. John Gay, who set all his words to English folk tunes and tavern songs. I don't promise it will be as good as Handel, but everyone says how amusing it is, and how cheerful the songs are, so I think it will do us all good!'

So off they went, and enjoyed themselves very much. Mamma thought the audience behaved very badly, spitting on the floor and eating oranges and shouting at the end of every song, and Papa thought the tunes 'rather inartistic', but Wolfgang and Nannerl were entranced.

'Fancy writing an opera about a highwayman!' Wolfgang said. The highwayman's name was Macheath, and most of the other characters were thieves and pickpockets. 'I never thought an opera could be so funny! One day I'll write a funny opera myself, you see if I don't.'

Concert engagements were becoming harder to get. 'I fear this kind and wealthy city is getting tired of us,' Papa worried. 'Well, we haven't done badly. But we must think of the future. If we can't give big concerts, I have another idea. We will invite people here, and charge them half-a-crown each to hear the children play, if Mr Williamson the landlord doesn't object to the noise.'

Mr Williamson didn't object at all, and so Papa wrote

an announcement in the *Public Advertiser*. Soon there was quite a queue of people in Thrift Street waiting to hear Wolfgang and Nannerl play. They generally bought some of Wolfgang's music, which Papa had had printed, and sometimes some concert tickets as well.

There was one very important concert they had to give, however. It was at the Little Theatre, Haymarket, on February 21st – and *both* of Wolfgang's symphonies were to be played!

'Please can I conduct them myself?' Wolfgang demanded. 'All grown-up composers conduct their own symphonies, so why can't I?'

'No, I don't think that's a good idea,' Papa said. 'It is good of the musicians to play the work of a boy of nine, but I think they might be annoyed if we put a baton in your hand. No, I think we must leave conducting to someone more experienced.'

Wolfgang was disappointed, but it was a great thrill to hear his first two symphonies, the very first things he had ever written for more than a dozen instruments, being played in public, and to hear the audience applauding when they were over.

Then – POSITIVELY LAST APPEARANCE OF THE MOZART CHILDREN BEFORE THEIR TOUR OF EUROPE, said an announcement in the *Public Advertiser,* and they began to practise for their last concert in London, in May.

Truth to tell, the 'tour of Europe' was far from settled. Papa wanted them all to go to Italy. 'A musician who hasn't been to Italy hasn't lived,' he said. But lately he had had several letters from the Archbishop of Salzburg, asking him when he was coming home.

'After all, dear,' Mamma said gently, 'he *does* pay you a salary for being his deputy Director of Music, and you haven't been at his Palace for over two years.'

'His Serenity is rich, and can afford to employ as many musicians as he pleases,' Papa replied obstinately. 'He must realise that it is my duty to devote myself to my children, especially to Wolfgang. He should be glad. By letting us travel abroad, he is showing that the Court of Salzburg gives great music to the world.'

But the visit to Italy had to be postponed, for one day, just as the Mozarts were packing their bags to leave London, a messenger came from the Dutch Ambassador with a letter. Papa opened it, looking very thoughtful. Presently he said, 'Children, it seems that we are commanded to go to Holland!'

'Holland?' Mamma made a face. 'That great flat country, with nothing but canals and windmills to look at! Oh, when are we going to see our dear Austria again, with its mountains and castles and lakes and pretty little churches? *Must* we go to Holland, Poldi?'

'It is the Princess Caroline of Nassau who invites us,' said Papa. 'And we can hardly refuse a princess. She has heard of our success in Vienna and Paris and London, and I suppose she doesn't want Holland to be left out. So, in a few weeks' time, my dears, we shall be in The Hague! At least I can give His Serenity the Archbishop a good reason for not going home yet!'

Mamma looked so sad and homesick that Papa added, 'Cheer up, my dear. We can have a short holiday first, for Sir Horace Mann, whom we met at Lord Thanet's, has invited us to stay for a month at his house in Kent.'

Then he sat down at his desk to write to Herr Hagenauer in Salzburg. 'Say some prayers for us, please, my good friend – for we are about to cross that terrible Channel again.'

9

Windmill Land

The meadows and cattle glided past very slowly. Too
slowly for Papa Mozart. 'What a country!' he groaned.
'It's barely thirty miles from Rotterdam to The Hague, yet
it takes more than six hours by barge!'

'At least it's cheaper than going by coach, dear,' said
Mamma.

'I suppose so. Forgive my impatience—but there is so
much to see in this country, so many art galleries and

lovely old churches – and all we can do is watch them go by!'

Poor Papa! It had been a long journey from England. The Channel crossing hadn't been quite so bad this time – only three and a half hours. In Lille they had all had colds, and it was three weeks before they were fit to travel again. At Antwerp Wolfgang had given a recital on the great cathedral organ. And now they were in Holland, on the way to visit Princess Caroline and her brother, Prince William of Orange.

The children didn't mind how slow the journey was. They had never before seen so many windmills, or such big ones. 'They sound as if they had rheumatism,' Wolfgang said. 'They make such funny groaning noises when the sails turn round!'

Nannerl stared in wonder at the strange clothes Dutch people wore; the men in baggy trousers and peaked caps, and the women in white headdresses like nuns, and everyone wearing clogs. And men and boys alike smoking pipes.

At last they reached The Hague, capital city of Holland, and very glad they were to get out of the barge and stretch their legs again. They were all terribly hungry after the long trip by canal, with only bread and cheese and apples to eat, and they were looking forward to a good hot supper at the 'City of Paris', the inn where they were going to stay.

The dining-room consisted of one huge table where all the guests sat together to eat. And what strange guests they were!

'I've never seen such dreadful table manners in my life!' Papa said as they went to bed. 'And the food – I haven't eaten such rubbish since that frightful place in Braunau we stayed at four years ago, on our way to Vienna!'

'Who are all these people, Papa?' asked Nannerl. 'The man sitting next to us at supper was a dwarf, and told me he turned somersaults for a living!'

'He belongs to a circus which is playing just outside the city,' Papa said. 'It seems that they haven't enough caravans for everybody, so some of the performers have to stay here. The pompous fellow sitting opposite me was an actor. He and his wife are in a play at one of the big theatres here. There were some musicians, too – I talked to a viola da gamba player, and took a cup of coffee with him.'

There was never any peace and quiet at the 'City of Paris'. Nearly all the guests were artists of one kind or another. The actor and his wife could be heard in their room, bellowing their lines for the play. The musicians all practised at once, and an Italian tenor sang scales in different keys at the top of his splendid voice.

Nothing ever disturbed Wolfgang. He just sat down amid all the din and began a new symphony. The noise made Mamma both happy and sad.

'Happy,' she said, 'because it reminds me of Salzburg. And sad for the same reason. Oh dear, shall we ever see our dear little home again? With all our good friends around us, and a house so full of music?'

Papa looked sad, too. He had just had a letter from Herr Hagenauer to say that their little canary was pining for them, and was refusing to eat.

'There's nothing to do but work, children,' he sighed. 'Perhaps, after we have finished our concerts in The Hague, we will do as the Archbishop wishes, and go home! So let us get on with our tasks with strong hearts! Come!'

Wolfgang and Nannerl now began rehearsing hard for a private recital they were to give at Prince William's

Court. But suddenly Nannerl stopped playing and put her hand to her forehead.

'I feel very strange, Papa,' she murmured. 'My head is so hot and my legs tremble. I think I am ill.'

'Another cold,' sighed Papa. 'These northern countries are so damp. Off to bed with you, child – you'll feel better tomorrow morning.'

But Papa was wrong. By evening Nannerl had a high fever. She couldn't sleep a wink, but lay tossing and moaning all night. Sometimes she talked wildly to herself in delirium. Mamma and Papa took it in turns to sit up with her, bathing her brow with cool water, doing everything they could to ease her pain.

In the morning Papa hurried to the Court for an interview with Princess Caroline. They knew no one else in the city. The Princess was horrified to hear of Nannerl's illness, and at once sent her own doctor, Professor Schwenke.

Professor Schwenke was a very old man indeed, and rather deaf.

'I'm sure he is the greatest doctor in Holland,' said Papa. 'But he drives me mad! He speaks only Dutch, and we can't understand each other. I've tried him in German, French and English, but it's no use. He has examined Nannerl, and keeps saying something in Dutch which I can't understand. And I keep trying to explain her symptoms to him, which *he* can't understand.'

At last the little old doctor's eyes lit up with an idea. *'Latine scis?'* he asked. 'Do you know Latin?'

'Satis bene,' said Papa. 'Well enough.'

'Bene, bene!' smiled the old man, nodding vigorously.

'They say King George the First of England had to talk to his Prime Minister in Latin,' Papa said to Mamma. 'I never thought, when I was beaten at school for not knowing my irregular verbs, that I would one day have to *speak* Latin to make myself understood!'

It would have been funny if it had not been tragic. For Professor Schwenke came out of Nannerl's room and took Papa aside. 'Herr Mozart,' he said. 'Your daughter is very seriously ill. I will do everything I can, but I cannot promise you that I can save her life.'

When Papa told Mamma, she went very white. 'Don't tell Wolfgang how serious it is,' she whispered. 'What about the concert on September the thirtieth? Ought we to cancel it?'

This was a public concert at the City Hall. Tickets had been sold, an orchestra had been engaged, everything was ready.

'No,' Papa said. 'We cannot cancel it as long as one of the children is fit to play. Wolfgang must see it through by himself. For one thing, we can't let the other musicians down, or the audience. And for another, it will take Wolferl's mind off his sister's illness. Nannerl is so sick, poor child, that she hardly knows what is going on; but when she does understand, I know she will want us to go ahead with the concert. She would be terribly upset if she thought it was being cancelled because of her.'

'But how can he practise?' Mamma said. 'The clavier is in the next room to Nannerl's – she cannot be disturbed.'

'He will have to practise in his head,' Papa said. 'By just reading the score and letting his fingers touch the notes without sounding them. He can do it. Anyway, the most important rehearsals will be with the orchestra, and I am sure the manager of the Hall will let him use the instrument there for practising by himself.'

Both Papa and Mamma were red-eyed and haggard with worry about poor Nannerl, who grew worse every hour. They could neither eat nor sleep for hours on end. Papa wrote to Herr Hagenauer, in Salzburg, and begged him to have special prayers said for Nannerl at St Maria Plain, the little church they went to when they were at home. At last old Dr Schwenke came out of Nannerl's room and said, 'I am afraid you must send for a priest. I think the end is near.'

Mamma burst into tears. Fortunately Wolfgang was away at the City Hall, rehearsing for his big concert next week. Papa tried to comfort Mamma. 'We mustn't do anything to upset Wolfgang's concert. Put a brave face on it, my dear. If it is God's will . . ."

The priest came. Nannerl was hardly conscious now. She was so thin and pale that she was scarcely recognisable. Her eyes were closed and she did not seem to hear what was said to her. The priest came out of her room again, looking very grave, and tried to say a few words of comfort to Mamma and Papa before he went away.

Suddenly there was a loud knock at the door, and old Dr Schwenke appeared, bringing with him a younger man.

'This is Dr Haymann,' he said. 'I have not yet given up hope, Herr Mozart. Dr Haymann has been working on several cases of fever like your daughter's. He has had remarkable success with his own patients.'

The two doctors spent several hours in Nannerl's room. What strange new medicines Dr Haymann brought, the Mozarts never knew. They only knew that for two days Nannerl lay very quiet, and slept peacefully. And on the third day she opened her eyes and asked for food.

'I do believe our prayers have been answered!' Mamma's eyes shone with joy.

'And the prayers of our good friends at home in Salzburg!' said Papa.

A few days later the City Hall rang with applause as

Wolfgang ended his concert. Papa was there with him, while Mamma stayed at home with Nannerl. Wolfgang and Papa came home in triumph that evening, and found Nannerl actually sitting up in bed receiving visitors.

'How are you, little sister?' Wolfgang asked. He always called her 'little sister', although she was five years older.

'Better, Wolferl! Oh, much, much better! But tell me about the concert! What did you play? Was the orchestra good? Did the audience like your new symphony? Tell me everything, everything!'

'It all went off splendidly, little sister. The audience were only disappointed because you couldn't be there with me. Get well quickly, you silly old thing, so that we can give some more concerts together!'

There were many more concerts in Papa's engagement book – at Amsterdam, Haarlem, and again at The Hague.

'In March the young Prince of Orange comes of age,' Papa said. 'There are to be great celebrations, with fireworks and feasts and all manner of things. Now I have an idea! Listen carefully.'

The little family, so far from home, hadn't been so cheerful and thankful for many months. Excitedly they made their plans.

'Do you remember the Dutch national anthem, Wolferl?' Papa asked.

'*William of Nassau?* That little tune we used to sing when I was a baby?'

'Yes. Suppose you were to write a set of variations on it, to be played before the Prince at Court; and perhaps you could string together a selection of Dutch folksongs, specially arranged for Princess Caroline's own orchestra; and perhaps a set of sonatas for the Princess, to thank her for having looked after us so well.'

So the land of windmills, which Mamma had thought

E

so flat and dull, celebrated its young Prince's birthday to the music of a ten-year-old boy. A rather homesick boy by now, who was very glad when he and his parents and sister at last got home to Salzburg, with the little river Salzach sparkling under the bridge, and the snow glinting on the distant mountains, and the long valley full of humpy hills with little castles on top. Home again, with Herr Hagenauer and his wife saying how much the children had grown, and all their friends and relations calling to hear the story of their adventures abroad.

Home again! But for how long? Wolfgang wondered. He remembered what Papa Mozart had said just before they left England. 'A musician who hasn't visited Italy hasn't lived.'

Suddenly the canary began to sing again, for the first time since the family had gone away. It sang and sang for sheer joy. It sang, Wolfgang thought, just like an Italian opera-singer. He had heard several Italian singers in London. He had always wanted to hear them in their own country – in Italy.

10

Italian Adventures

The coach climbed higher and higher up the zigzag mountain road, and soon the wheels hissed and crunched and skidded in the deep snow. All around was blinding whiteness. Wolfgang looked down upon the glittering icy valley they had just left, with the river winding through it and the little town of Innsbruck looking like a fairy-tale city, full of delicate steeples and tiny streets and bridges.

Papa was beating his arms across his chest, trying desperately to keep warm. But Wolfgang was so entranced with the wonder of setting out on a new journey that he

forgot it was the middle of December even though his ears
were almost dropping off with cold.

Now they had reached the top of the col between two
vast mountain-sides which disappeared into the clouds
above them. This was the Brenner Pass – the gateway into
Italy. The coach began to descend the road on the other
side, rocking and bumping wildly.

'That fellow drives much too fast,' growled Papa. 'He'll
overturn us all if he doesn't take more care.'

Wolfgang laughed. 'He knows I'm on board, Papa.
And no coach can ever be too fast for me! Cheer up, Papa.
Let's practise our Italian!'

So they began speaking Italian to each other, just as they
often did at home, although they had never been to Italy
before. Sometimes they slipped into French or even
English, just for fun. They had travelled so much that
foreign languages came naturally to them.

It was nearly a week since they had left Salzburg. This
time poor Mamma and Nannerl had been left at home.
'Nannerl is a fine musician,' Papa said, 'but music is not
a career for a grown-up girl.'

'Poor old Horseface!' Wolfgang said. 'I suppose she'll
go and marry that dreary Herr von Mölk who's always
gazing at her with cow's eyes and sighing his heart out.'

'Herr von Mölk is a very decent, reliable young man,'
Papa said sharply. 'She could do a lot worse than marry
him. Anyhow, she is far too young to marry anyone. And
I wish you wouldn't call her Horseface. She's an extremely
pretty girl, and you should be proud of such a sister.'

'Oh, I am,' said Wolfgang seriously. 'She's a very good
little sister indeed, and I have been a good boy and written
her a letter every day since we left Salzburg.'

He began to sing a tune from *Bastien and Bastienne,* a
little opera he had written last summer in Vienna. Papa

at last managed to laugh. 'You may be a "wonder of nature" at a piano or an organ, Wolferl, but God forgot to give you a voice!'

'I'm singing in octaves,' Wolfgang said. 'You can only do it once in a lifetime – when your voice is breaking!'

'Well, don't, please,' Papa groaned. 'It sounds terrible!'

It had been hard for Mamma to say goodbye to them. There had been tears; she had implored Papa many times not to forget to take his liver pills and Wolfgang to write home regularly. But she would have Nannerl to keep her company, and her beloved home. 'No more European tours of three years,' Papa had promised her. 'We'll be back within eighteen months, I promise you!'

Their adventures began at Roverto, where Wolfgang gave an organ recital in a church which was so full of people that he could hardly climb into the organ-loft. After a day or two, they went on to Vienna, where the same thing happened. Journalists came to interview him, and Italian ladies sent him flowers.

Papa, as usual, found something to worry about. 'Don't think I'm not proud of your success, Wolferl,' he said seriously. 'You know how anxious I have been that you should be recognised in Italy. But you have still plenty to learn, and I don't want you to get a swelled head.'

'It is very pleasant to receive flowers from ladies,' Wolfgang grinned. 'Especially when they are wrapped in poems – and the poems have money sewn into them!'

'Money?' Papa gasped. 'What do you mean?'

'I mean that Italian ladies are much more tactful than people are at home,' Wolfgang said. 'They know that musicians are poor, and so – but see for yourself!'

He held out a small packet containing four ducats. 'I found it in a bunch of roses which Signora Sartoretti gave me when we went to lunch with her yesterday!'

'But we can't accept money from her like that,' Papa said uncomfortably.

'It pleases her to give us a present of four ducats,' Wolfgang smiled. 'Why shouldn't I accept it? Indeed, I think she would be offended if I didn't!'

'Oh, well,' Papa said resignedly. 'Four ducats is four ducats!'

At last they arrived in Milan, where they stayed at the monastery of San Marco.

'Oh, how good it is to have really warm beds to sleep in!' Papa said thankfully, as they breakfasted on soup and bread and hot chocolate. 'The good monks always look after us better than any hotel! Do you remember how we enjoyed ourselves at Ybbs when we were on our way to Vienna seven years ago?'

Wolfgang shook his head. 'No, Papa. It is all so long ago – and I was only six.' He sighed contentedly. 'Now at last I can really get on with some composing. In Verona my fingers were so cold I could hardly hold my pen!'

'I'm hoping great things of Milan,' said Papa. 'We have an introduction to Count Firmian, the Governor-General of Lombardy, who wrote me a very nice letter about my book on the violin. He has heard a lot about you, from our friends in Salzburg. We are to have an interview with him tomorrow.'

Count Firmian received them very kindly. 'We must certainly try to arrange some concerts for this young man,' he said, looking very keenly at Wolfgang in a way Papa didn't quite like.

'Is your Excellency displeased in some way?' Papa asked.

'No, no, my dear Mozart.' The Count coughed awkwardly. 'You must forgive me for saying this, but I should like to hear the boy play first – and also to test his skill in composition.'

'May I assure your Excellency –' Papa began; but the Count raised his hand for silence.

'You know the musical world, Herr Mozart. There is much jealousy, much gossip, and I must tell you frankly that certain people have suggested that – well, that there is some kind of trick about this boy's performance. He is still very young, you know – only fourteen years old – and it is very difficult for people to believe that a boy of his age can write symphonies –'

'If those rogues in Verona have been spreading false-hoods about my son –' Papa began angrily; but again the Count held up his hand.

'I should just like to have the boy to myself for an hour or two,' he said. 'We will give him certain tests, and if he does them well, I myself will announce that all the rumours are false, and that he is ready to take his place in Italian musical life at once.' Seeing Papa's face growing quite red with anger, he added quickly, 'I have no doubt, Herr Mozart, that all will be well – and that your boy is worthy of his father, whose excellent book on how to play the violin is used by every music teacher in Milan!'

What could Papa do but smile and bow politely? The Count took Wolfgang to a private room for a few hours. Here he met Signor Sammartini, a very old man who had taught some of the best musicians in Europe, and Signor Piccini, whose very modern music Wolfgang had often heard. They asked him a lot of questions, made him play the clavier and the violin and the organ, made him improvise and write music on the spur of the moment.

When they rejoined Papa, they were all smiling and seemed in a very good humour indeed. 'Herr Mozart,' said Count Firmian, 'there is absolutely no doubt whatever about your son. He has mastered music so easily that it is not surprising that people cannot believe it.'

He took Papa aside and outlined his plans. First, Wolfgang was to compose some songs specially for a musical party the Count was giving at his Palace in a few weeks' time. 'If they are successful,' the Count went on, 'as I am sure they will be, I should like the boy to write an opera for me. The opera season begins at Christmas, so he would have eight or nine months to write it in. Except, of course, the main songs, which he will have to talk over with the singers in the weeks before the performance. Now, how does that fit in with your plans, Herr Mozart?'

'We are greatly honoured, your Excellency. I could not wish a happier commission for my son!' Papa smiled. 'Our plans are uncertain — we shall probably visit Bologna, Florence, Rome and Naples — but whatever happens, we will be back in Milan in good time for rehearsals.'

'The trouble is,' Count Firmian said, 'that the words aren't written yet. Suppose Cigna-Santi, the librettist, were to send them bit by bit as he writes them — you could send us your music by post, also bit by bit. How would that be?'

'Just as you like, sir,' Wolfgang said. 'It doesn't worry me.'

'Then it's all settled,' the Count smiled. 'Oh, by the way, I almost forgot to tell you what the opera's about. It's about King Mithridates of Pontus — but don't worry your head about that. The important thing is to write the music so that it suits the voices of the singers!'

The musical party was a very grand affair. All Milan society was there — the Duke of Modena, the Archbishop of Milan, and all the leading musicians of the city. Wolfgang's songs were a great success; and when the concert was over, everybody went on to a fancy-dress carnival.

'Imagine,' Papa wrote home to Mamma in Salzburg, 'capering about in fancy dress at my age!'

Wolfgang and his father left Milan with the March

winds blowing, spent a week in Bologna, and then went
to Florence.

In Florence it was already spring. Papa's enthusiasm
knew no bounds. 'It is every bit as beautiful as people say!'
he said, as they looked out of the window of their little
room at the inn where they were staying in the famous
city. Churches, palaces, monuments, statues, picture
galleries – for two whole days Papa did nothing but walk
about the city, looking and looking, feasting his eyes upon
decoration. Wolfgang got rather tired of it – he was never
much interested in any art except music – but he enjoyed
climbing Giotto's bell-tower, all 414 steps, and gazing at
the view from the top. Poor Papa, whose legs were not as
tireless as his son's, only reached the 100th step, where he
stood gasping for breath.

Everything they saw in the shops – leather, silk, jewel-
lery, books – was wonderfully made and decorated. It was
as if the Florentines simply couldn't make anything that
wasn't beautiful.

At last, on the third morning, Papa said, 'Come, that's
enough sight-seeing. To work! Our ambassador in the
City, Count Rosenberg, has asked me to call upon him.
He has recommended us to the Grand Duke of Tuscany,
who is our Emperor's brother, and who heard you play in
Vienna last year. There's no nonsense *here* about whether
you're a conjuring trick or not! You are to give a concert
on April the second at the Court.'

'All by myself?' asked Wolfgang in alarm.

'No.' A slow smile spread over Papa's face. 'With
Nardini!'

'Nardini!' Wolfgang almost jumped through the ceil-
ing. 'He is in Florence?' Nardini was the most famous
violinist in the world.

'He certainly is, and he'd like you to accompany him in

a sonata or two. And then you are to give your own recital on the clavier, and with a bit of luck the orchestra may be persuaded to play one of your symphonies.'

Wolfgang was really excited now. 'Do you think he would give me a few violin lessons while I'm here?' he asked.

'If he has time, I'm sure he will,' Papa replied. 'He's a very decent fellow – I met him once in Vienna, years ago. Oh, by the way, Rosenberg says there's a pupil of his who has had a great success in Florence. A young Englishman called Linley. He'll play too.'

'Linley? Not the Mr Linley we met in London?' Wolfgang was puzzled. 'The one who lived at Bath?'

'No – his son, Tom Linley. He's the same age as you.'

Wolfgang felt a momentary pang of jealousy. 'The English can't play the violin,' he scoffed. 'They make splendid horn-players, but it takes an Italian or a German to understand the violin.'

'Wolfgang!' His father spoke very sharply. 'You're talking utter nonsense. There were excellent violinists in London, and you know it. Do you really think the Florentines are so stupid that they can't recognise a good violinist when they hear one? Could *any* pupil of Nardini's play badly? I ask you!'

Wolfgang burst out laughing. 'I'm sorry, Papa.'

'I've told you before, Wolferl, I don't want your success to go to your head. Success doesn't last unless you make yourself a better musician every day. That was why I was glad to hear you say that you wanted to have some lessons from Nardini.'

The concert was one of the longest and most brilliant Wolfgang had ever taken part in. It went on for five hours. At the end of it, Signor Nardini and the two boys were recalled over and over again to take their bows.

They all had supper together after the concert. Wolfgang found himself liking the dark, thin-faced English
boy more and more. It wasn't only that he was a good
musician. His manners were so free and easy. He could
talk of so many things besides music. Everything about
him reminded Wolfgang of his good times in London
five years ago.

'It's strange that we never met in London,' he said to
Tom. 'I remember your father – he came to our concert
in Spring Gardens, with Dr Burney.'

'We nearly met once,' Tom smiled. 'I came to hear you
at Ranelagh that summer afternoon. My mother took me.'

'But why didn't you come and speak to me?' Wolfgang
asked.

'Oh, I suppose I was too shy,' Tom grinned. 'You
seemed so grown up, and you were surrounded by such
great people – people like Dr Johnson – and I knew I
couldn't do half the things you could do.'

For a moment Wolfgang felt ashamed. He had been
jealous of this generous, modest boy who had nothing but
praise for him.

'What a pity we didn't meet then!' he said. 'We could
have given concerts together – Linley and Mozart.'

'The two boy prodigies!' Tom laughed. 'Well, we may
do that yet! If not in Italy, then at home in England.
Promise me you'll ask your father to arrange it with Mr
Nardini, or with my father! Oh, we could have such
great times together! They tell me you've been asked to
write an opera, Wolfgang – for Milan next season! You
must bring it to London – or better still, write one specially
for London.'

Watching the boys together, Papa Mozart and Mr
Nardini exchanged a smile. 'This is good for Wolfgang,'
Papa said. 'He hasn't enough friends of his own age.'

At last it was time to go to bed. 'What about a ride before breakfast?' Tom suggested. 'We can hire horses from a riding school near here.'

'I'm – I'm afraid I can't ride,' Wolfgang said awkwardly.

'Well, let's go swimming, then!'

'I can't swim, either,' Wolfgang muttered, feeling suddenly very small indeed.

'That's all right – I'll teach you!' Tom laughed. 'And we'll ride donkeys down to the Arno. Anyone can sit on a donkey. I know a place where we can be alone, about two miles out of the city. You needn't worry – nobody will see you! Shall we say half-past six tomorrow morning?'

Next morning, the hills around Florence were glistening with dew, and the sharp early-morning air, laden with the smell of flowers, tickled their nostrils like snuff as they jogged along. Wolfgang felt a new thrill of excitement, a love of being alive that for once had nothing at all to do with music.

'If you can ride a donkey, you can ride a horse,' said Tom. He looked at Wolfgang critically. 'A bit small for your age, aren't you? You ought to take more exercise.'

Now if anyone else had drawn attention to his smallness, Wolfgang would have been bitterly offended. But somehow with Tom Linley it didn't matter.

They arrived at a stretch of river where the trees bent over almost touching the water, and the banks were thick with bushes. They peeled off their shirts and, wearing only breeches, waded into the rippling water. Tom struck out strongly for the opposite bank, and was across in no time. Poor Wolfgang stood shoulder-deep splashing about uncertainly. With a shout of laughter, Tom plunged in again, swimming under water, and reappeared, spluttering and panting, at Wolfgang's side.

'Now watch me and do as I do,' he said. 'Lean forward

on the water—let your legs float up—breathe regularly, like this—'

Tom watched the Austrian boy's thin white arms and legs thrashing about in the water. So this was the famous Wolfgang Amadeus Mozart, who had taken London by storm five years ago!

'Try again — push your legs out and back like a frog — don't hold your breath—*andante,* not *presto*!—that's better. Bravo! You see, you swam four whole strokes then!'

They lay on the grass, panting, letting the sun dry their bodies. Wolfgang had never in his life felt so free.

'You know, Tom, I've never done the things normal boys do,' he said. 'It was always practise, practise for the next concert — and moving on to another city next week, and composing whenever I had a moment to spare.'

'If I had your talent, I wouldn't worry about not being able to swim!' Tom said.

For perhaps the first time in his life, Wolfgang found himself envying another boy. Tom's parents were fairly well-off, he guessed. Tom hadn't had to work for his living from the age of six onwards, touring Europe, putting up in dingy inns, often being treated like a servant by the patron who was paying him. He wouldn't have missed it for worlds—yet there was something missing, perhaps.

'Breakfast,' said Tom. They dressed and clambered back on to their donkeys. As they jogged back to Florence, laughing at anything and everything, Wolfgang knew that he would never forget this friendship with the English boy. Someday, they vowed, they would give concerts together. Someday, Wolfgang promised himself, he would go to England again — perhaps live and work there permanently, as Johann Christian Bach did, as Handel had done.

11

Long Live the Little Master

But when would he go again to England? Not yet, probably not for many years. For already the Mozarts had to
leave Florence.

'We have to be in Rome for Holy Week,' Papa said.
'It is something I have always longed to do – and besides,
they will have the most wonderful church music there,

music one cannot hear anywhere else in the world. And we have invitations, too – from many great families there who want to hear you play. And after that – Naples, perhaps. I have an introduction to the Court there.'

Wolfgang said nothing. He had enjoyed Florence more than anywhere else in the world, and he had found a friend.

'Don't look so sad, Wolferl,' Papa said gently. 'We will meet other English friends in Rome – people who were good to us in London.'

When they got into the Rome coach, Tom Linley came to see them off. 'Promise you will write me a letter every week, Wolfgang,' he said, gripping Wolfgang's hand until it hurt. 'I want to hear all your news.'

'I will indeed, Tom,' Wolfgang said huskily. 'Will you still be in Florence if we should come back this way?'

'I don't know. My father wants me to go back to England to school when I have studied a little longer with Mr Nardini. Or else I shall go on a tour in Germany – I simply don't know.' He shrugged and smiled.

Rome was almost as wonderful as Florence – only everything seemed so much bigger. But any city would have seemed wonderful after the journey there, in the most appalling April storms they had ever known. Once the coach broke down altogether, and they had to spend the night at an inn in the mountains above Orvieto, sleeping two in a bed and fourteen in a room, with all manner of tramps and pickpockets.

Soon after they arrived, they went to the Sistine Chapel in the Vatican to hear the choir.

'They are going to sing the famous *Miserere* by Allegri,' Papa said. 'No other church in the world has the music or knows exactly how to sing it. This is something you cannot hear anywhere else in the world, Wolfgang.'

Wolfgang was suitably impressed as he listened to the
Pope's own choir singing. It really was extremely beautiful. He was looking very thoughtful as they came out into
the spring sunshine. When they got home to their hotel,
Papa Mozart saw him get out a sheaf of music paper. He
sat down and, sticking his tongue out of the corner of his
mouth as he had always done ever since he was very small,
began to write at a furious speed.

An hour later he showed his father what he had done.
'What's this?' Papa laughed. 'Not your Milan opera,
surely?' He read the opening bars and gasped. 'Wolfgang!
This is the *Miserere*! You – surely you didn't steal a copy?'

'No, Papa. I just remembered it and wrote it down.'

'But every note seems to be here! Even that last chorus
for nine voices!' Papa was horrified.

'I'm sorry,' Wolfgang said. 'I thought you'd be interested
to have a copy.'

'But you have stolen music from the Sistine Chapel!'

'I haven't really stolen it, Papa,' Wolfgang smiled.
'Think of all the millions of people who will never be
able to come to Rome! Don't they deserve to hear it,
too?'

'I don't know, I really don't know,' Papa muttered.
'What are you going to do with it?'

'Nothing much. I'm going to send it home to Mamma
as a souvenir of our journey!'

'The Archbishop of Salzburg must never know of this,'
Papa frowned. 'I really don't know what to say.' He
looked at his son in wonder, and then sighed. 'Well, only
you could have done it!' He looked at the manuscript
again. 'See how beautifully these parts are interwoven.'
He shook his head, lost in admiration. 'After all,' he said,
'it is only *copying* which is forbidden in the Church. There
is no rule against writing the *Miserere* out from memory!'

One particularly strange adventure they had in Rome. As they were coming away from Vatican City after an audience with Cardinal Pellavicini, they saw a ragged fellow sitting on the pavement and grinning at them. 'Signor Mozart!' he whined. 'Signor Mozart!'

If the wretch hadn't called him by name, Papa Mozart would have hurried by. There were so many beggars in Rome that you couldn't possibly give them all money, or you would have become a beggar yourself at the end of a day.

'Papa!' Wolfgang cried in astonishment. 'It is that man who took us across the Channel when we sailed to England – the man who carried our bags, and found us a coach at Dover.'

'Oh yes, young sir!' the man grinned toothlessly. 'Emilio Porta at your service, gentlemen!'

'Good heavens, man, but what a state you're in!' Papa said. 'You look so ill. Times have been hard for you, I can see!'

They had indeed. Porta had wandered through France, taking odd jobs wherever he could. Then he had joined the French army in Corsica, and, disliking it, had deserted, got on to a fishing boat at Bastia and made his way to Elba, and so to Italy. He wanted to go back to France, where there was more money and more work, but he couldn't afford the fare, and it would take him many weeks to walk.

'Let me be your manservant, Signore!' he begged. 'I will get new clothes, I will do you credit.'

Papa Mozart didn't trust him an inch. Porta would probably steal those new clothes – he certainly couldn't afford to give them to him. Papa put his hand in his pocket and gave Porta all he could find there. At once the fellow's face lit up, and he was again the cheerful rogue who had looked after them so well when they had first seen the white cliffs of Dover. As they had a valet already, they kept Porta for fetching and carrying jobs.

So it was Porta who saw them off in the coach to Naples. For two days he refused to let them go. 'There is a gang of highwaymen who have been attacking all coaches on the road from Rome to Naples,' he warned them. 'Yesterday a postillion told me that the leaders had been either killed or captured by police and soldiers. Perhaps it is now safe to travel.' He rolled his eyes dolefully. 'But I wouldn't risk it if I were you, Signore.'

'He is just telling us that so as to keep us in Rome a few days longer,' Papa said suspiciously. 'I told you I didn't trust him.'

When at last they climbed aboard a singularly rickety coach for Naples, Papa was relieved to find that they were sharing it with four monks.

'You are in good company, Signore,' Porta grinned and touched his hat as they tipped him. 'No bandits will dare to attack you now!'

And indeed none did – for at least half a day. Then, as dusk gathered, they heard a shot – and another shot. The driver, instead of stopping, whipped up his horses to a breakneck speed. A deafening shot rang out just above their heads, and the monks began to pray in Latin.

'There's nothing to fear,' Papa said tensely. 'That was our postillion firing back.' The coach began to lurch violently as it gathered speed, and poor Wolfgang was flung to the floor.

There were more shots, and much shouting; and at last the noise died down, and the foaming horses drew up at a wayside inn where they spent the night.

Next day they were in Naples. It was terribly hot, and from the first moment Papa hated the city. 'A dirty, godless place,' he said. 'I would not have come here if I didn't hope that we might give a concert before the Royal Family here.'

But the King and Queen could not, or would not, see them. They filled in the time sightseeing – the ruined old Roman cities of Pompeii and Herculaneum, and the crater of Vesuvius. There were more parties, more invitations, especially to the houses of the many English families who lived there, many of whom remembered Wolfgang's concerts in London five years ago.

One day there came a letter with a seal which made Papa's eyes open wide when he saw it. His hand shook as he gave it to Wolfgang. 'Open it,' he said in a low voice. 'It's for you. From the Vatican!'

Wolfgang looked at the beautiful script inside which must have taken some clerk all day to write and decorate. 'The Order of the Golden Spur,' he read aloud, puzzled. 'What on earth does that mean?'

'It is one of the highest honours a musician can receive,' Papa said quietly. 'Gluck is the only other Austrian who has ever been given it. And you are certainly the only boy of fourteen who has ever won it!'

'Shall I have to go to Rome?'

'Of course. We must leave Naples at once and wait upon His Holiness.' Papa Mozart looked at his son in a puzzled way. 'You don't seem very excited about it. Don't you understand? The Pope is going to give you a kind of knighthood. In future, Italians will call you not Signor Mozart, but *Cavaliere* Mozart!'

To his surprise, Wolfgang burst out laughing. '*Cavaliere* Wolfgang Amadeus Mozart! Heavens, how they would laugh in Salzburg if I went about calling myself that! Well, I'll be a *Cavaliere* in Italy if you like, Papa, but not among my friends at home.'

Back to Rome they went, so fast that the coach nearly overturned, and Papa Mozart twisted his leg badly; and then to Bologna. For in Bologna another honour awaited Wolfgang – one that he valued far more than being called *Cavaliere*.

'*This* is the honour I have always wanted, Papa,' he said. 'Something which only great musicians can confer upon a fellow musician. The Philharmonic Academy of Bologna is going to elect me a member! There's only one thing I want more than that. I want my opera to be a success in Milan!'

That opera was already beginning to take shape. He had been scribbling odd bits of it on coach journeys and in taverns for weeks. The librettist, whom he had never met, sent him bits of the text by post, in envelopes that often had to be forwarded from city to city until they reached him after several weeks. And Wolfgang posted odd pages of the music back to Milan in the same irregular way.

Everything at the Opera House was in a glorious muddle when Wolfgang and his father arrived in Milan. Two singers who had been engaged months ago didn't turn up because they had been offered better money somewhere else.

'I had hoped our old friend Manzuoli, whom we met in London, might be able to sing for us,' Papa said, 'but he has another engagement in Germany. And I don't know what to make of the prima donna, Signorina Bernasconi – she has a brilliant voice, and says she likes your music very much, but I keep hearing rumours that she wants someone else to write her big arias for her. I think I'd better have it out with her.'

So Papa went to see her. He came back in great good humour. 'It's just as I thought,' he said. 'You always get this sort of thing in operatic circles. Apparently there's an older composer who is jealous of you, and he's furious because *he* wasn't commissioned to write this opera. So he's been going to Signorina Bernasconi behind our backs and trying to persuade her not to sing your music. I think I've settled his hash all right.'

But there were still troubles. Signorina Bernasconi wanted a lot of alterations in her songs. 'You see, Signor *Cavaliere,*' she said flatteringly to Wolfgang, 'I can sing nearly an octave higher than this *coloratura* passage you have written for me. The Milan public knows this perfectly well, and they will be expecting to hear it. Now suppose you were to take me up to top G in this bar – and then I'll do a long trill on it, and you can keep the orchestra waiting until I come down to top C.'

'I had to do what she wanted,' Wolfgang said to his father afterwards. 'I don't think it spoils the music too badly, and if it helps to make *Mithridates, King of Pontus* a success, it's all to the good.'

Then the leading tenor, Signor d'Ettore, came to see them. 'This really isn't good enough, Mr Mozart,' he said. 'Your son has given the baritone more arias than I have got. Now who, I ask you, goes to the opera to hear a baritone, unless he's a comedian? It's the romantic tenor that captures their imagination. Now I suggest that you rewrite these two songs in my range, and give me a few bars of *falsetto,* towards the end – the audience will simply lap them up.'

In the end, they compromised by giving Signor d'Ettore *one* more solo. The only problem left was Signor Santorini, a very fat singer who arrived in Milan only three weeks before the opening night. He took an instant dislike to Signor d'Ettore, and it was a terrible job to persuade them to sing in a quartet together with the baritone and the *prima donna.*

Poor Wolfgang was exhausted by the time the opening night arrived. He had rewritten parts of the music so many times that he was sick of them. He was conducting the opera himself, so he had to rehearse the musicians himself.

'There are two Germans in the orchestra,' he groaned, when telling his father all about it. 'They keep having rows with the Italians and calling them *macaronis*! And some of the Italians don't like the music, and say they won't play such "barbarous German stuff"! And one or two of them are furious at being ordered about by a boy of fourteen. I have to keep on sending for the manager of the Opera House to restore order among them all!'

Still, as so often happens in the theatre, everything was 'all right on the night'. As soon as the opening chorus and the first aria were over, Papa Mozart, sitting anxiously in his box with Count Firmian, knew that it would be a success. And what a success! The audience went wild, clapping and shouting in the middle of Signorina Bernasconi's top G so that the end of her solo couldn't be heard at all. They encored so many songs that, by the time Act One was over, it looked as if the opera would take all night. And when the singers assembled on the stage to take their final curtain, the audience began shouting: 'Wolfgango Mozart! Wolfgango Mozart!'

Wolfgang went on to the stage, the orchestra (who had been making so much fuss about being conducted by a boy of fourteen) stood up and joined in the cheers, and up in the gallery people began shouting hoarsely, over and over again, *'Evviva il Maestrino!'* ('Long live the little Master!')

With those shouts ringing in their ears, Wolfgang and his father decided to take a holiday. It was the first they had had for many years. In Turin, Padua and Venice, they were invited to parties, they went to other people's operas, they had the time of their lives. In Venice, wealthy families lent them their own private gondolas to go wherever they liked.

But one day Papa said, as he usually did, whenever they had been enjoying themselves, 'Enough of this! It's high time we were going home. Soon, Wolferl, you will have to think about getting a regular job. You can't go on being a boy genius for ever. Besides, home is home. All the travels in the world only make you love your own home more.'

Wolfgang nodded his head vigorously. 'I want to see Mamma and Nannerl again, and the Hagenauers, and all our old friends in Salzburg – and I just want to see their faces when we tell them all our adventures!'

So home they went, over the snowy mountains in a lurching stage coach, until at last they looked down upon the fair valley of the River Salzach, and the misty hill-tops with little castles and churches perched upon them; and the higgledy-piggledy town of Salzburg, with its steeples and cobbled streets. Soon they would be home, in the warm little third-floor flat in the Löchelplatz, where Wolfgang had first picked out tunes on the battered old clavier, and the canary still sang for his supper, as all musicians everywhere must do.

12

What Happened Next

Well, there *was* a job for Wolfgang when he got home.
A new Archbishop (his name was Hieronymus von
Colloredo) made him 'concert-master' at the Palace, at a
very small salary. But Archbishop Colloredo didn't think
much of musicians. He treated them as servants, and
made them eat in the kitchen. And he was much stricter

than the old Archbishop had been about letting his Court musicians travel abroad, which the Mozarts had to do to earn more money.

I haven't room to tell you *all* the things that happened at the Court of Salzburg, but one thing is important. Ten years later, when he was 25, Wolfgang had a famous row with the Archbishop which ended in his being literally kicked out of the Palace. No doubt the Archbishop thought Wolfgang a conceited young puppy who had been spoiled by too much success when he was young; but I think that by refusing to accept bad conditions of work, Mozart was striking a blow for all musicians everywhere. Things were already different twenty-five years later, when tough, eccentric old Beethoven could be splendidly rude to the rich and powerful, showing them that musicians were equal to anyone under the sun.

Yes, the wind of change had blown through Europe. Artists and musicians, in Wolfgang Mozart's time, depended largely on patrons to give them work and pay them for it. But the French Revolution in 1789 shook the power of the aristocrats everywhere. (In that Revolution, I am sad to say, poor little Marie-Antoinette, whom Wolfgang had met in Vienna when he was six, and who had become Queen of France, lost her pretty head at the guillotine.)

I have still sadder things to tell you. How could a musician who began so brilliantly die at the early age of 35 – of overwork and an illness which was undoubtedly made worse by not having enough to eat? Prince Kaunitz, Prime Minister at the Court of Vienna, used to say, 'We really ought to give Mozart a pension. Such men are born only once in a hundred years.' But nobody ever did, though the Emperor saw to it that his wife Constanze got a little money when she became a widow.

Mozart married Constanze Weber when he was 26 and she was 19. He had been in love at first with her sister Aloysia, an opera singer, a flighty girl who was only interested in her career and in marrying a much richer man than Mozart. But he soon got over it and learned to love the quiet little sister who was much better suited to him. I hope you will one day read his letters to her, full of jokes and affection and cheerful nonsense. I'm afraid Constanze wasn't a very practical wife, and always overspent her housekeeping money; and their life together, though happy, was full of ups and downs – mostly downs. Poor Mozart, friendly, generous, impulsive, was a bad business man – quick to borrow, quick to lend, easy to swindle, and always too much in need of money to be able to bargain for a good price for his work.

In those days, composers had to work so fearfully hard for their money. There was no 'royalty' system by which they could go on getting a little more money every time a symphony or an opera was performed anywhere in the world. You were paid a lump sum, cash down, when you had finished the composition, and that was all. And people got tired of everything so quickly. 'Something new' was the eternal cry from the public.

People didn't talk so much about 'art' in those days, either. Music was a craft, almost as being a carpenter or an electrician is a craft. If you were a composer, you were asked to write things at top speed for special occasions, such as a serenade for a Duke's wedding, and once the wedding was over, everyone forgot the serenade. Believe it or not, Mozart never had the slightest idea that any music he wrote would ever be remembered after his death.

Well, today, if you switch on the wireless and twiddle the dial, you are almost certain to hear something of Mozart's being played somewhere. His wonderful, gay, witty operas – *The Marriage of Figaro, The Magic Flute, Don Giovanni;* his symphonies (nearly 50 of them); his piano sonatas, which you will certainly play if you have piano lessons; music for the church, tiny little light bits and pieces of music for dancing which he turned out to order for the Archbishop of Salzburg's private orchestra . . . this extraordinary man wrote over 600 different compositions of various shapes and sizes.

'Your son,' said that Grand Old Man of music, Joseph Haydn, to Leopold Mozart, 'is the greatest composer I know.' When Papa Mozart heard that in his old age, he knew that all the sacrifices he had made for Wolfgang had not been in vain.

Lastly, a very brief word about the music itself. Some people think it is 'sweetly pretty', full of elegant decoration, as if Mozart were a dandy in a periwig writing for fashionable people alone. Well, it isn't, and it shouldn't be played like that. It is crammed with life, energy, tragedy, comedy, courage, hope, wisdom and wit.

If you don't know it at all, start with *Eine Kleine Nachtmusik* – 'A Little Serenade' – in four movements, which musicians generally agree is the most perfect small set of pieces in the world. And please get someone to take you to one of the operas, at Sadler's Wells or Covent Garden (or, best of all, at Glyndebourne). You will laugh until you fall out of your seat at some parts, and others will give you wonderful tunes that you will take away and remember all your life.